To Beryl

Happy Christmas
2020

Roux
by
John Stirling

ISBN: 978-1-8382223-7-6

Published By: -

i2i
PUBLISHING

i2i Publishing. Manchester.
www.i2ipublishing.co.uk

Roux

The majestic red squirrel
who befriended
the King of England

by John Stirling

Contents

To

Dame Judi Dench & June Brown MBE
For their kindness, their invaluable generosity
and support for projects over so many years.
Now it's time for them both to meet

"Roux"

John Stirling

"The Marrow Of Life"

Just over forty years ago the 'Daily Express' went on a crusade to cover a very sensitive story of immense heart ache with serious consequences. It was headlined - 'Tragedy of a Loving Mother'.

Liz Bostic's devotion to her family came under enormous pressure as she lost her youngest boy to a Bone Marrow disease. Then, her husband was diagnosed with lung cancer and, soon after she was herself to receive the news that she too had cancer. She then had to deal with the fact that her eldest young boy also had Bone Marrow disease with a very short-term prospect of life. She took her own life. Her husband was left distraught having to look after Simon now five and take on the fight.

The headlines had a tremendous impact. I asked if I could be of help which received support and I was able to produce 'The Night of a Hundred Stars' at Drury Lane Theatre Royal, later to become known as 'Simon's Show'. Simon Bostic was the first child recipient of a bone marrow transplant and I can't explain how it felt when last month I received a call.

"John, how's it all going?"

The mere fact that he had survived and was still with us was something I can't relate in words; still frail with on going surgical needs.

"How's it going with you Simon?".

"OK, although the medics warn me all the time not to expect to much."

I was quick to respond, " That's what they said over forty years ago!"

'Roux' is dedicated to you.

God Bless - John.

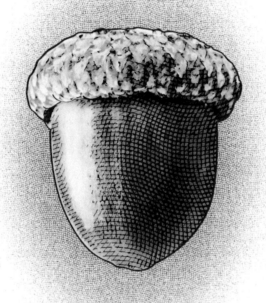

The Majestic Small Red Squirrel who Befriended the Young Tall King of England

Inheritance

Life and fame have always attracted stimulations to be placed together for a meaningful reason.

The belief in oneself can be adopted by both from adulation being opposed by gentle thoughtfulness.

'Life' follows a rich pattern of natural strengths and weaknesses allowing nature to take its own course. Perhaps easier and less rewarding in some areas but outweighed by honesty and love.

'Fame' Is promoted by desire, a furtherance of ambition which finances a talent or a gift.

Finally, accomplishing ultimately self-appreciation of oneself at the expense of others with no valued truth. To comprehend entirely from time to time.

The two come together and help each other dismantling the excess and unnecessary.

Replenishing and mixing a small particle of both succeeding in sharing a common value to the benefit of both.

That is what transpired when a gentle rodent came face to face with a majestic ego and together formed the most extraordinary alliance.

'Life' Where children benefitted and inherited a world worth living.

'Fame' Where children inherited cruelty in trying to make a world worth living in.

Welcome to Roux

These matters are of importance to accept before handing the findings to more analytical minds, to read in the hope of presenting solutions.

It was on the balcony at Hampton Court Palace that the work was done quietly, discreetly in what Thomas Wolsey referred to as 'The Silent Get Together'. Visually exciting, verbally incoherent and there for everyone to see – a unique format for success.

Henry VIII would not allow freedom of speech. All discourse had to be in obeyance of an order, whether acceptable or not. Criticism was banished, suggestions discouraged or in most cases forbidden. Time allocated simply for acclamation and flattery. Henry's wealth was his comfort, ownership his power, dominance his acceptance, philanthropy his quest. The young king was renowned for revelling in undisputed control, an overriding criterion that painted his life colourful and entertaining. Exciting to a nation, his popularity gaining unequalled degrees of admiration.

There is little doubt that Roux experienced the best years with the young Tudor King of England. A time of unprecedented wealth allowed for the conception of creative adventures, in turn generating larger than life characters. Fortunes were welcomed for extraordinary projects and designs, leaving a legacy of unsurpassed grandeur in which the next generation could delight.

Roux had taken his chance from Henry's philanthropy when having accepted the lease on the Royal Oak. He had been encouraged to renovate and modernise the property to stately home status, even though he was just a lone squirrel with no special needs. Still, the King suggested that he acknowledged his new standing in life, make inroads into now living an appropriate lifestyle. Roux always felt the size of the tree a little awe-inspiring, in many ways accentuating loneliness, but his motivation for the project remained. It seemed he was being directed to do his best and impress, always conscious that he would more than likely never again be given a chance such as this. He spent many joyous days there, exercising - when safe to do so - on the sweeping deer lawns, along the fast-flowing brooks, using the outings to sharpen his claws as well as his brain. He left marks on numerous barks as he scaled everything in sight, irrespective of its origin or age.

Henry VIII glided into adulthood unnoticed. There was an inward desire for him to activate his architectural skills and artistic behaviours; he would have loved to work on the wonderful Palace itself but it did not belong to him – a dilemma Wolsey was quick to put right by presenting Hampton Court Mansion as a personal gift, allowing the King to acquire the Palace and elevating Wolsey to the highest position in the land.

Unknown to Roux, Henry had forged new borders around the forests and woodlands to enhance the royal hunts, now gaining popularity being led by him. To this monarch a sport of monumental importance. With new boundaries drawn out, the area designated would mean the loss of many oaks and surrounding habitat, destroying Roux's long-standing family home. The squirrel would now have to negotiate with a great intelligence, of which he inherited from his father, having left a legacy of strong parental guidance should such matters ever arise.

So came a moment in history when two institutions formed an alliance. The times they spent together were of dear value. For six years, outlooks and sentiments were shared between the oak and the balcony – a tribute to their bond and the mutual respect it housed, without a word spoken. The private audiences held in the open air above the Palace overlooked the splendour of sixty acres; manicured lawns, parks, and grounds, a landscape Henry had already set his heart on reshaping.

Their meetings were vibrant, a unique and somewhat obscure get-together. Both were keen for forward planning, though always in pursuit of meaningful encounters, broaching the welfare of both the kingdom and the realm of the country's wildlife. The monarch was confident that he was in the company of the perfect ambassador.

At this point, I realise only too well that for some, this adventure is inconceivable. A much-loved, inexperienced monarch, better known for his strength, agility and intellect, recognised by his subjects for his resounding authority and command, is, in later life, epitomised predominantly for his obscure choosing of matrimonial partners. He is now so ungraciously remembered and unfairly branded, it is a travesty to some members of the animal kingdom whom he served so valiantly in his youth.

So, accept. Believe in memory of Roux.

Prologue

The seeds of glory

There comes a time, rare but indisputable, when a great test enables us to distinguish what is truly important from all that is fleetingly desired, which has so often mistakenly been given pride of place in our lives and our ambitions. After a short pause and reflection, we have to look forward to the rebuilding of our common life as a necessity, a debt to the next generation who is owed a helping hand, all the while being able to accept an influence of untold experience, which may go some way to encourage an ability to rule.

A capacity in the belief that death is not the end, that past lives have not been wasted; they have an inheritance of hope so we can dream of what our country, our world of nature, will look like in a mirrored image of those gone before.

Roux was sadly missed by his community in the grounds of the Palace. His daily appearances a much-valued accessory to the formal life within the unique surroundings. It had taken him time to fit in, but much like King Henry, he had soon become acknowledged as the emblem of his own kingdom – born to lead, his organisation unequalled, his attention to detail impeccable, the loyalty he showed to his King and Queen unrivalled. He heralded and sustained all the qualities Henry VIII yearned for with his messages of hope.

It would be a falsehood to believe Roux was uncommunicative, that was certainly not the case. His vocal interpretations from a variable selection of warnings, along with his firm and competent general signals were easily distinguished, detected gratefully by those for whom they were meant. Roux had little or nothing to lose. He could come and go as he pleased, ultimately it was his choice.

Henry would not seek advice from his squirrel. At the end of the day they shared certain qualities, joviality being a favourite. Seriousness was avoided but attempted when necessary, affection in abundance. All proving successful in living normally, which Henry had little chance of experiencing, but on which Roux based his whole existence.

Roux would sit and accept the kind and overly-generous invitations with his built-in ability to keep the King entertained, sitting opposite his giant shelling acorns, nibbling at seeds, admiring the chestnuts, destroying the pine cones while always listening with ear tufts poignantly forward – a deceivingly visual look of interest at what was being said. In all honesty it meant very little to him but allowing the King to behave in an unprecedented way, creating a stable and therapeutic foundation that no other individual could achieve.

The red squirrel would use body language, which was of vital importance to him in his natural habitat. Over time, it became clear, that as he moved closer to the King, the monarch would relax. He would enjoy the closeness, accepting the signs, exposing a certain trust that the mammal exuded so brilliantly. Roux would move up on to his shoulder and sit near his ear, giving Henry comfort with the feel of his tail brushing the side of his face, often encouraging a tactile moment by sitting in the palm of his hand accepting small offering, something his majesty adored. All this unbelievably conveyed a sense of calm. There was never a demand, he was never opposed. He was free to just open his thoughts as never before, the results astounding.

● ●

The emblem of his Kingdom, *'Born to lead'*

The year is 1509. A young eighteen-year-old prince learns unexpectedly as his father Henry VII takes his last breath, making his final proclamation. He talked of the crown, focusing on its immediate transfer of power and accession to the throne of England.

Overnight, the teenage monarch is unwelcomely having to accept the responsibility that his future life is now about to take on. A perilous journey dominated by the rule of law, encapsulating the most stringent sense of duty to a country yearning for adventure.

England was in fact peaceful when the young King ascended to the throne. He had entered into a family of steadfast stability. Forests and woods were seen as the lifeblood of the nation, maintaining a good quality of air, furnishing wildlife with preservation, covering large areas of land with canopies of foliage and allowing animals from the red deer to the red kites with roe and boar to roam free.

In a sprawling expanse of thick woodland, with heathland punctuated by autumn throwing its ruddy blaze of sun on the oaks, larches and sweet chestnut, all well-concealed in a region that marked their place, pronounced their identity welcoming them into a society in which they so very much belonged.

Amongst all this noble surrounding, a unique family of red squirrels enjoy the tranquillity of the idyllic setting, the signatures at the base of the aged oak strewn with chewed pine nuts and empty acorn cases, announcing the occupants are thriving but acknowledging that life around is pronounced and harsh. The red squirrels have always valued their ability to live aloft, high in the pine, but always maintaining a conscious sense of respect for the oak, which is majestically in such abundance in their royal hunting grounds.

This is their story. A short life that they shared together. For young Henry, a fleeting association when he was in such need of someone he could trust and who could offer advice, to affectionately direct the monarch in sign language, uncompromising loyalty without a single word spoken. For Roux, a journey of distinction, addressing his unique ability to communicate by gesture and inference, a genuine care without orality. Great patience and effort from both parties translated to a successful partnership, culminating in unseen magic, and heralding a special liaison that brought the natural world in line with the fabrication of wealth and power, what some might like to hail as the real world, but with Roux would empathetically disagree.

Chapter One

The King and I

Roux's decision to leave home had been thought about for some time and planned in detail. He was just anxiously waiting for a change in the adverse weather conditions to make his monumental departure a reality. Anticipating a break in the monotonous rain that had scuppered his initial itinerary and put it on hold, he had now been given extra time to contemplate long and hard about the effects that were going to unravel before him. A canvas of blue sky would have been of value, giving him that extra boost of confidence that he needed.

It was, in many ways, an unwanted and unenviable decision to have to make, leaving the comfort and security of a good home, but there was now little choice. Roux had to deal with this maturely, confidently relaying a certain optimism to offer some consolation to his mother. She would, above all, be conscious that she might never set eyes upon her son again. The separation was necessary for life to unfold, as predicted by his supportive parents.

His mother had built a happy home. She was determined to ensure that Roux and his two sisters should have every chance and advantage that was at her disposal. It would prove overwhelming for all young squirrels to first venture out into the world. It would be physically demanding, often at times painful – a constant battle. Diligence was of the utmost priority for moving forward and collecting food, maintaining vigilance with the demands of a commanding defence and strong authority when those around are trying their hardest to invade and steal. The hard times have to be covered, individuality must always prevail, be seen by all to be a major quality not to be usurped.

Roux had always enjoyed being an integral part of his family. He had proven to be popular, a trusted member of society. He was never happier than when playing with his two sisters as they shared the freedom, the joy that went with their convivial surroundings. His parents were both intelligent and affectionate. They had made quite sure that he was well-equipped and grounded for both his own survival and, in time, when he was ready for that special someone who he might choose to share his future life with.

His departure date had been looming for some time, and the possibility of home sickness had been a constant worry to his doting parents. His mother had compensated her impending loss by giving more attention to the two girls, which was inevitably one of the reasons for Roux to take his leave. The home was warm and welcoming but confined in space; it became clear as the children grew that there was a lack of privacy. Life was becoming practically impossible for them to share fairly. It was down to the eldest to make the first move, to present the departure with courage and fortitude, giving the girls an insight into inheriting the same quality when it was their time to leave.

Roux had not expected that on leaving he would be making such a long outward-bound journey. He had barely left the confines of the family meadow which had served him so well in his childhood when he was faced point blank with the arduous task of discovering his new home. He had inherited his father's building prowess, his initiatives, ability, and acumen in putting things together rapidly and in a do-it-yourself manner around the tree. Whereas from his mother, he had inherited her architectural and creative ability in making something from nothing, and finalising with an extraordinary array of home accessories.

The first day had been hard, Roux covered over three and a half miles before he was able to rest. He scratched out a shallow grave and burrowed himself into the base of a hedgerow, sharing his first evening with young fledglings, busy singing in their new nests, well-camouflaged among thin twigs and gorse, waiting eagerly and less patiently for their parents' speedy return.

Apprehensive of any dangers that may unveil in the night, Roux thankfully fell asleep, exhausted in the hope of getting through his first ordeal unscathed.

The second day was spent navigating farmers' fields and avoiding the men working on the land, cautiously clinging to the hedgerows and wicker fences erected to keep the land free of animals and conserve the farmers hard-earned living. He came to rest by a babbling brook. The sight of fast-flowing clear water was a pleasant surprise of which he immediately took advantage. Beside the stream stood a weeping willow, majestically bowing over, its branches just inches from the water. It was a truly lovely location for a stop. For a moment, Roux considered settling there, building something for himself, but was ultimately doubtful that there would be enough room to furnish him with the interior requirements, plus the units to set down permanent roots. Otherwise, his journey could well have come to end here.

The last day of his seemingly epic pilgrimage was spent investigating the habitat. He needed to source his food; hunger was now bearing down on him. Flooded with choice, and now responsible for only his own likes and dislikes, Roux was able to peacefully select, without any pressure from others, his intake of new and obscure vegetation. Deciphering it all for himself was a challenge, but one he found exciting, often drawing on his mother's early guidance.

Roux eventually came to what he thought might be the end of his long trek across country as he found himself facing a large ornamental wrought iron gate elevated from the ground. Covered in ivy and surrounded by overgrown grass, it looked as if it hadn't been used as a means of entry for some time. The curious squirrel parted some of the ivy. Peering through, he saw a long, straight avenue of beautifully manicured trees making an impressive driveway, supported on both sides by sprawling, undulating lawns. The landscape was well attended to, making the whole spectacle the most impressive driveway.

Slowly and cautiously, Roux made his way up the avenue, sticking closely to the verges. Feeling a little safer, his gaze falls on the lawns that reach as far as the eye can see, dotted with small bushes and neatly trimmed hedges, enclosing the sixty odd acres of land as something of great splendour. In the centre lay a circular pond with a huge water jet shooting into the air, forcefully returning the water downwards to be reclaimed by the pond. More gardens lie ahead of him. In the distance, arising from the landscape and making a formal announcement, the magnificent vista of a stately home. A country mansion of sheer elegance, accentuating the need of all the cleverly designed acres adorning it and bringing it to life. Unaware of his discovery, Roux had in fact landed unconsciously into Hampton Court Mansion House.

The prospect of going any further didn't occur to him, he had a feeling he had reached his destination. He couldn't imagine finding anywhere else to match this outstanding opulent estate, but the question he posed himself was where to start looking for a bolthole, allowing him somewhere to rest and digest his exciting new location and to figure out his next move. He opted for an enchanting tree which seemed to welcome him with open arms.

Roux was now gaining a newfound confidence as the grandeur and amazing sights were unfolding before him with every turn he took. Suddenly, the unassuming squirrel turned a corner and found himself faced with a sight of indescribable strength and power, triggering memories of home, albeit incomparable in size but reflecting its lineage. What he saw could only be described as the most outstanding oak tree he had ever set eyes upon. The width of the trunk was an unimaginable scale. Grained and worn, heading towards the sky, majestically splitting halfway up into a crown to allow the thick branches to disperse. The branches thinned towards the top of the tree, with younger immature twigs and branches filling the gaps, appearing ready to fall, but in Roux's previous experience they would still take his weight for many weeks to come, having spent a misspent youth using them to scurry from branch to branch, sometimes even saving his life and his honour by making themselves accessible for the odd quick recovery from theft and unwanted predators.

The red squirrel's architectural talent now came into practise. He just couldn't help himself, running up and down its magnificent frame. He dashed along the branches now in search of locations and an entry, feeling that he couldn't be the only one to have discovered this sanctuary of greatness. There was sure to be an opening to this old mature giant. It wasn't long before he found an entrance of sorts – a cavity, which had evidently been excavated many times by the hundreds of claw marks and discarded nesting strewn around, neglected.

On closer inspection, it needed a lot of work and restoration. How he wished now that his father had been available to advise in his hour of need. Roux needed to make the ultimate decision of what was possible and what to discard. There was plenty of clearing to be done, floor space to be uncovered, but the fundamentals were definitely in place and the structure was sound. Here was the beginning of a new and exciting adventure, one which he could have never been imagined. An address to die for.

Roux was now showing signs of exhaustion. It was fast becoming evident that he had taken on more than he could manage single handed. His adrenaline, nervous energy, and his young enthusiasm was too much to sustain, now taking its toll. Although he was quite sure he had found the right place, nobody as yet had interfered with his tenancy or claimed previous occupation. He was still living on his nerves, trying to secure and establish a permanent lease for his future existence. The project was of an enormity he had not foreseen, his youthful experience was testing his ability. He realised, from his childhood, how his parents often had to battle against seasons when predators or other rodents searched for sanctuary for winter or spring. When breeding programmes were of high priority, with space at a premium, it was always a dangerous time. This sort of location would be at the top of everyone's list. The fights for territory that emanated in defence of their realms could be fatal, strategy and execution being at the forefront of any small victory. But with determination and a clear sense of purpose, Roux just kept his claws crossed and hoped for the best.

The first weeks had been set apart to excavate the interior of the massive trunk. A daunting prospect, one which Roux attacked with renewed energy, vigour and determination. Inside his Great Hall, the first requirement was to construct a suitable flooring. After digging out all of the debris and levelling off the ground, he put down a layer of thin twigs as a foundation. Then came the arduous task of collecting and transporting hundreds of rotten acorn shells lying all around the base of the oak, laying them meticulously on the twigs, forming a base to support the autumn leaves he had retrieved, dried, and kept safe for some time, ready to position and finish off the carpet of comfort. He found moss and lined the inner walls, making the carpet stable and unmoveable to keep the warmth in. The grafting squirrel then faced the task of cleaning the walls. They were of considerable height, requiring all his acrobatic abilities. All this leading to the opening at the crown of the tree, where the branches sphered off in different directions. Fortunately, where the branches took over there was a gap, a window, which enabled a narrow ray of light to shine through on a good day. Not enough to light the great hall in its entirety, but sufficient enough for him to work and complete his mission.

Considering his youth and inexperience, he was seemingly accepting that the renovation and reconstruction of this majestic, aged monument was now of importance. He was, in squirrel terms, adhering as best he could to planning requirements and regulations, attempting with all his efforts not to do anything to jeopardise this structure of historic value.

The Great Hall was completed in two months. His concentration was then centred on the upper branches and passageways, all leading to the upper floors which he had designated for food storage and sleeping quarters. Before moving onwards and upwards, he spent considerable time and effort on the main entrance, which he had now enlarged to get all the basic requirements into the trunk. He now had to fill in the cracks and make the front door a strong, narrow cavity which could only just take his frame if he squeezed through forcefully, making sure that no uninvited visitor could wander in. The defence of the realm came as a priority to this small and considerably talented rodent, and in his view a necessity. He had no other means at his disposal to introduce any other security system at this time in the proceedings.

The upper floors were not in need of such scrutiny. There were no openings or floors to lay down, darkness would be welcomed during the heavy winter months. The larder was well-hidden at the very top of the tree, impossible for anyone to access unless they had prior knowledge, which he felt sure he had dealt with.

It now came down to insulation and decoration, something he was going to have to think about rather than rushing blindly into it and making an unjustified mess. The thought of having to start again to amend any mistakes was something that he didn't relish, so he went back to his study to draw up his final plans for total completion.

It was an early morning, a single ray of sunshine infiltrated Roux's only window.

Outside, the mist was slowly dispersing off the mansion grounds. The dawn chorus was being overtaken by individual calls, gathering momentum as the extra few hours of daylight appeared as a welcome overture to a new day. A celebration for Roux, now able to finalise works on his new home.

(

Due to the intricate refurbishment programme Roux had set himself, he was partially ignorant as to what was taking place outside. He had been aware for some time that there had been a commotion around the trunk of the oak, but he had not felt it necessary to investigate. He was entirely fixated on completing his home.

Thomas Matchett was the head gardener at Hampton Court. Along with two of his plantsmen, they had been set the task of building an oval bench surrounding the entire width of the tree trunk, for members of staff and guests to relax in the fresh air, taking in the panoramic view of the sixteen acres. It was a project devised by the owner of the countryside mansion, Thomas Wolsey, in an attempt to elevate the status of the home, and thereby promoting the estate, of which he had grown so proud.

Roux ventured furtively outside, making sure the workmen had finished for the day, and made his way down the bark. A light breeze blew some leaves from their overnight landings. They drifted down, landing softly on the new bench, already heavily laden with acorns. Roux could tell that few friends and neighbours had ventured out so far today. He examined the new furnishing and its smell of freshly chopped wood, feeling the need to leave his first scent mark of the evening upon the bench, not only to attract others but to officiate its welcome arrival. The nestling acorns were clean for once, having avoided hours on the damp grass, courtesy of the dew. They were ready for cracking and consumption, no further work to be done – a real treat for a working squirrel.

As Roux sat benefitting from the gardener's hard work, the sun took its first real initiative of the day, climbing higher, now enveloping the enchanting tree. The squirrel had spent so much time indoors and hadn't had the chance to experience fully this vision of strength he had inherited. The cloudless canvas of blue sky above now highlighting the masculinity of this Royal Oak. Bearing an age of over a century, it had become a bastion of integrity, carefully planted just a few yards from the mansion's private apartments. On summer evenings, it offered a cooling shade, and was now about to welcome the mansion's staff of over one hundred on the infrequent occasion when they were allowed to join the Royal Family and enjoy a respite together, as a break from their arduous hours of working indoors. This rare opportunity was a brief chance to distance from protocol which they otherwise so rigorously maintained, allowing for a well-organised interval spent with their King and Queen, who personally acknowledged the labourers for their loyalty and hard work, a display of gratitude from the crown.

The Royal oak symbolised diversity. Beneath its branches people discussed matters of importance   prattled through trivialities and mundane conversations. Picnics frequented the afternoons with brightly coloured parasols and blankets spread over the lawn. The privilege of being in the company of their sovereigns was, a culmination of their work. To be in a relaxed conversation with the couple, without any affectation, was a pleasure. The young king always conveyed a gentleness towards his employees, and a public affection towards Catherine's presence. He was by no means a lady's man but nonetheless expressed an immaturity that the women staffers found charming. These rare evenings were allocated generous times. It became a joyous distraction, the royal couple sharing anecdotes of their lives for their staff to relay at home to those eager to of the private and precious encounters.

The youthful king, although newly appointed, had proved himself remarkable for keeping routine. His schedules. Carefully managed by Wolsey, who relished the extra authority, rescued the monarch from tedious and strenuous duties, allowing the king his valued leisure time. Being young and sportive, the monarch often tackled the tree to its heights. His conquering of the oak was met with applause by onlookers below and left those who were employed to ensure the king's safety anxiety ridden; they stood, braced with Bated breath and their eyes locked on the monarch. Their lives and employment where encased in his welfare, but the praises of those spurring him on proved more influential than the concerns of the sceptics. This young man was adventurous, and the oak gave him strength. It was there to be challenged. The

King was able to sit atop the tree, high in the branches, overlooking the wondrous view. This lively recess took him far from the monotonous tasks of ruling.

It was on one of these evenings that the King settled on the bench, under the canopy of leaves. Sitting quietly, he took the time to regain some sanity after a trying day of urgent royal duties that even Wolsey found stretching. A rustling from inside in the oak broke the meditative silence. Henry took notice, gazing at the tree. He heard scratching then, again within the oak. It was a distinctive sound, but its cause wasn't obvious. Perhaps a bird, thought the King at first, but as the scratching persisted, it sounded heavier, with what can only be described as spirited intentions. Whatever creature was creating the disturbance was doing so with purpose. Building work was well underway within the Royal Oak.

The King sits motionless, expectantly hoping that the tree's inhabitant will appear to introduce themselves. He waits for some time, the ruckus from the tree getting progressively more intense, causing a slight tremor in the branches. The tree starts to shed unwanted twigs and debris, mud and sawdust escaping from its cavities with no regard to anybody below, covering the King of England in unwanted building matter.

Henry was determined to see this mystery to its end. He dispensed of all his responsibilities, allowing Wolsey the privilege of dealing with it all in his absence. The King endured a long wait for the instigator of all the mess to finally make an unannounced appearance.

A small red head appears out of the Oak's main cavity. With pointed ear tufts on alert and his nose taking in the scents, he assessed whether an excursion beyond his new home was safe. If misjudged, revealing himself any more could prove fatal. He eased forward cautiously, ready to vanish at the drop of an acorn.

At first glance, Henry is prepared to accept this was the occupant of the Oak, but the din from inside made him curious as to whether this was truly the property's only tenant. After some time and having bolstered confidence, assuring himself that the coast was clear of predators, Roux prepares himself to squeeze through the cavity, taking a gamble on a safe exit. It was a tight squeeze, but he pushed through until the full rustic coat emerged. He took a few moments to shake off the dust, finishing with a grand finale. His majestic tail was unleashed, flowing right up his back and falling gently over his head, presenting a white blaze in a plume of rust with an ermine finish.

Roux clambered out, visually exhausted. He sat upright, wiping his eyes to clear away the grime, attempting to regain his vision in the bright daylight. Without moving a muscle, the King experiences something special. The tail settles in its upright position, just towering over the squirrel's head, the plume cascading over its shoulders and back. The red squirrel emanated a royal standard. The monarch, used to such grandeur, considered it a pleasure to be in the company of an equal. The regal two observed one another, both seemingly recognising the other to be someone special, someone to be treated with equality.

To Henry VIII, it seems this striking animal has chosen Hampton Court Mansions as his birthright, his heraldic accession. Strangely, the King is enchanted, prepared to accept and honour the status quo, bringing this special squirrel into the family. A Tudor squirrel is born.

■■

Roux is to become of great importance to King Henry. He is graciously accepted onto the royal balcony each morning for daily briefings, he is introduced to Queen Catherine, a fine-looking woman with resplendent red hair, matching her husband. With the charming squirrel now in the picture, all three now stood beside one another, exceeding in good looks and nature.

On the balcony outside the King's bedroom, a silver salver of nuts and other squirrel favourites is left every morning and evening. Roux could easily manage the hop across from one of the overhanging branches on to the parapet to reach it.

Henry finds Roux a calming presence, brightening his early mornings before having to turn his attentions to matters with disturbingly cruel outcomes – duties of unbelievable power for a man who had barely entered adulthood. Facing such matters is a difficult job for a monarch with little experience, but thankfully Henry was strong and decisive in his rule.

Roux was forced to maintain his monastic existence, compelled to devote his entire days to finishing the home that had come to mean so much to him. Having now accepted a bachelor status, his thoughts turned to the future. Perhaps the time had arrived for him to share this paradise with someone of his choosing. He felt it was time for his life to take on new meaning, one more worthwhile and rewarding. During the long months of construction, he had come to feel a loneliness. Leaving home had taken its toll. Roux believed now that his squirrel life would benefit from a companion.

The hardest thing Roux had to accept concerned ownership of the Royal Oak. Despite his hard work, the truth was that the tree could never belong to him. For now, it was time to enjoy the fruits of his labour.

The time was right to find a wife and start a family. A Tudor dynasty of his own.

Chapter Two

A Full English

Bacon, eggs, robins, tortoise, badgers, otters and seagulls.

Roux was stirring earlier than usual. The evening before he had found a generous amount of dry hay in a neighbouring field. He transported it over, albeit laboriously, taking him over half a dozen journeys to carry it all back to the tree for him to make a warm eiderdown. He had retired earlier than usual to take full advantage of the new insulation. Come morning, the cosy squirrel was reluctant to tear himself away from the newly acquired central heating. Eventually, he amassed the courage and dismantled the eiderdown in sections, so as to not allow the early morning chill to give a shock to the system.

Darkness prevails with an uneasy quiet. The curtain of mist was slowly lifting, giving just enough light to uncover the grandeur of the grounds. The silence and stillness are preparing to be extinguished by the dawn chorus – a melodic charm from a mixed orchestra performing wondrous calls in perfect harmony, a daily occurrence.

As the outdoor chorale reached its climax and the voices trailed away, Roux's attention was drawn to a small flicker of candlelight emanating from the upper windows of the mansion, initially from the servants' quarters. He followed the journey taken by the candles, flickering weakly now. Moving slowly from window to window, they were making their way through the labyrinth of corridors, finally reaching the staircases leading to the kitchens below, returning the corridors to darkness.

Like the King, the squirrel was a late riser. He was intrigued at what was unfolding before him, he had never witnessed it before, these tasks were usually long completed before he awoke. Intrigued, he journeyed, half-awake, the short distance to the gatehouse and into the courtyard, where the main kitchens were situated.

The doors to the kitchens were always kept open due to the immense heat from the furnace fires, allowing Roux was able to peer inside. He faced the main kitchen, being lit by the young scullery maid, the youngest member of the staff. She was the one to rise before anybody else, tending to her most important task of making light so the workforce could get on with the first meal of the day – The Royal Breakfast. The young maid travelled clockwise around the room, carrying with her a chair on which she climbed to reach the wall candles with her taper. Working through over forty candles took the best part of half an hour. When she finished with the walls, she climbed onto the heavy working table to light the three hanging chandeliers, situated right above, which stretched the length of the main kitchen. Her last task, after descending from the heights of the table, was to light the two enormous furnace fireplaces. Having already been built up with large logs, they were prepared for instant combustion, ready to heat the three hanging cauldrons, set to boil water and send heat through to the other three smaller side kitchens.

Roux now noticed the young kitchen staff gathering, finishing their epic journey as they finally entered the main room, extinguishing their candles and placing them on the back wall. They each made their way to their appointed positions, ready for the elaborate breakfast preparations.

The kitchens are run meticulously with military precision. Two young pages appear at the door in full uniform, standing out amongst the working pinafores with red and gold jackets, finished in gold braid with gold epaulettes, white knee breeches, stockings and buckled shoes. They part in the doorway, allowing the three housekeepers to pass through followed by four assistant chefs and pastry cooks, heading off to put together this morning's menu and start cooking.

The kitchen maids gathered the morning's requirements. A mix of ingredients, so the chefs can prepare their individual specialties to later present to the monarchs. Robins, pheasant, tortoise, badgers, otters, and seagulls together made a royal favourite, and if the King had left any remnants of swan from yesterday's dinner, then it would feature on this morning's breakfast tray.

The young scullery maid is exhausted now, her arms and legs aching, burn marks on her knuckles from the dripping wick. It was time for her to give her focus to her final job, for which she was specially chosen. The King, aware of the young girl's care for the welfare of the local wildlife, personally requested the young maid to see that the red squirrel was well-catered for. It was a rarity for such a job to be prescribed to someone so young, but Henry believed this young soul was to be trusted.

She placed the silver salver onto a small table, loading it with a selection of nuts, seeds and acorns. She was certain that Roux would relish the assortment. Roux looks on gratefully at the young girl, sad that he has never as yet had the pleasure of meeting her. He decides there and then that he would acquaint himself with his personal chef as soon as the opportunity arises. She displays the salver beautifully, everything in tiers. The effect was mouth-watering. Roux shuffled on his feet, impatiently, knowing it would be a while before it reaches him on the balcony.

The first tasks of the chefs is to ensure the pages can leave on time with the King's breakfast, followed after fifteen minutes by the Queen's first meal of the day, her lady in waiting stood at ready with the scullery maid. It's a long journey for the pages and they aim to arrive on time to both chambers. They take a discreet approach, prepared to find their majesties either together or in separate apartments. This has to be relayed, with no delay, to the lady in waiting, who would need to be held back by another fifteen minutes.

With everything adhering to the chefs' requirements, the two pages set off from the kitchens. Roux decided to follow from outside, scaling and scurrying along the walls, ivy, parapets and the roof, tracking the staffers the whole way as they march through the corridors and climb several flights of stairs until reaching their destination – the royal apartments and the bed chambers.

The objective of the two pages is to keep a marching step through the corridors and staff quarters, maintaining heavy-sounding steps all the way along the wooden floors on their half mile marathon, their heavy footing announcing to all remaining staff, courtiers and private guests still asleep in their rooms that it is now time to rise. Their majesties are due to commence their working day and the time has come to assume their positions in readiness for royal commands and other matters of urgency for which promptness is required.

The pages turned their final corner and faced the last corridor, fitted with rushed carpets. They relent their stride as they near the private apartments, avoiding making too much noise. Reaching the imposing oak doors, they soften their approach and enter the King's bed chamber, waking the sleeping sentry who had been on duty all night as they pass.

The royal mass under the bedclothes stirs reluctantly, slowly reorientating himself after a good night's sleep. The pages stand motionless, observing by the window and waiting until they are certain the monarch is alone, having once received the wrath of the King for not allowing the Queen a dignified exit. Eventually, the King finds a way out of the mountain of crumpled blankets and deerskin covering. The pages relax, approaching the monarch with the overladen tray, placing it by his side as he manipulates all six foot into a comfortable position to receive his meal.

They both bow and retire, thankful that there are no requests for their return journey. Starting their walk back, they once again take up marching, taking through the same route, passing the staff rooms. Their heavy footing reiterating that the Royal Breakfast has now been delivered. It's time to rise.

Simultaneously, candle at the ready, the Queen's lady in waiting sets off, leaving the confines of the main kitchen for her equally long journey. She carries her own tray, heading for her majesty's private apartments along the East Wing of the house, a notoriously difficult journey as part of the route is in need of substantial repair. The Queen's tray is decidedly lighter in its content than the King's, with a substantial amount of meat being replaced by a generous selection of the Queen's favourite fruits, neatly displayed around a tureen of hot soup, kept to temperature by a silver oval lid exhibiting the royal coat of arms.

Following the lady in waiting is a scullery maid carrying a large porcelain basin full of tepid water, with a serviette and towel draped over her frail shoulder. The small demure youngster opens and closes all the doors along the route, never releasing her tight grip on the porcelain basin. She walks carefully, as still as one could be while in motion, with strict directives not to spill a drop.

Catherine of Aragon is an exceptionally attractive woman of Spanish descent, regarded by the nation and courtiers as a beauty. They envied her, now the Queen of England at the age of twenty-three, married to the youngest King. She presents herself well at royal functions, standing tall next to her King, youthful and endearing to her country, who had faith in the ruling of the couple. Their success is evident when their subjects don't hesitate to bow or curtsy upon their entry – a demonstration of sincere respect and affection.

The day was in its infancy. The lawns and gardens below remained colourless, overshadowed by impending daylight, making its way through, bringing with it a new hope as the day finally dawned. Roux had been waiting for some time for the silver salver but had grown impatient and returned home to deal with some personal matters.

Henry stood on the parapet of the balcony with the silver salver, waiting for his visitor to arrive. He gazed at the tree for some time, in awe of its strength. He waited a further few minutes to see if Roux surfaced from the tree, but it was not to be this morning. The King decided against leaving the salver out on the balcony, conscious that the birds may take advantage of the offerings. Not wanting to let his squirrel friend down, Henry left the core of his apple, in the hope that Roux would accept it later in the day.

Henry closed the window and left the salver on his dressing table, leaving his staff with the explicit instruction that it was to be left there until he returned that evening, when it should be replenished with fruit and breadcrumbs.

******

Later that week, Henry returned, tired and weary, from a two-day hunting outing at Windsor Great Park. The trophies were already on display to be admired. He washed down his exhausted horse in the yard, publicly grooming him before leading him away to his stable, something he always insisted on doing personally, both out of respect for the animal who had served him so well, and to show the grooms and stable lads how it should be done. Henry was keen to keep a camaraderie with the men, who were also accomplished riders. He would often at times lower his guard, joining in their banter. The riders were grateful of the King's generosity with his time, they enjoyed his company, but could never fully relax. They couldn't forget that they were in the company of royalty.

Reaching his private apartments, Henry eager to shed the heavy clothing he had had on his back for forty-eight hours. He removed his boots, pouring himself a mug of ale. When he looked up from his feet, he was surprised to find the Queen stood before him, anxiously requesting his attention. Her brow was furrowed, it was clear that she was upset.

Catherine urged the King to sit down. She sat opposite him, trying to gauge his mood. Henry shifted in his seat. It wasn't often that the Queen would bring her problems to him, she was usually one to resolve matters on her own.

The Queen's eyes began to fill up. As tears rolled down her face, the young King grew more uncomfortable, hoping that one of his staffers would enter, giving him reason for escape. Still, he kept focus on his Queen, unable to waver from his strong, regal persona. Through her tears, Catherine explained an incident that had occurred in the King's absence. The Queen was victim to theft, and following investigation by the housekeeper, it had become evident that the young scullery maid had committed the offence. The Queen felt the seriousness of the matter called for his majesty's intervention. Henry was intrigued, although he hoped that his involvement wouldn't be required for long. He was hungry and saddle-sore, longing to lie down.

The Queen had opened her jewellery case and was beside herself upon noticing her beloved squirrel brooch, gifted to her by Henry some time ago, was no longer in its place. She and her lady in waiting carried out an extensive search, but still they couldn't find it. They concluded that the brooch had surely been taken from the Queen's possession unlawfully. After the housekeeper investigated the theft, The Queen was shocked to find the young scullery maid brought before her. She had, after all, only ever extended kindness and generosity to the young girl. She was reluctant to bring the matter to the King, conscious of the honours that he bestowed onto her, but such an act could not be brushed aside. Henry would become aware of the disappearance anyway, since he would inevitably ask his Queen why the brooch had not been affixed to her clothing.

Henry was sympathetic, willing to assist in any way he could. He would need time to consider a suitable punishment. Catherine had agreed with the housekeeper to keep the young girl's crime as a matter of privacy, undisclosed to the staff, and handle the matter with sensitivity. The brooch had already been returned. The Queen was adamant that the child should not be paraded in front of his majesty in his official capacity, that would simply terrify the girl.

Winona Trackett was brought before the Queen in her private apartments early, accompanied by the lady in waiting and the housekeeper, stood either side of the fear-stricken young girl.

Catherine was feeling a certain compassion; she was a forgiving soul. In her official role, however, she must maintain a visible strength, an unwillingness to respond too leniently. She had dressed down, so as to not intimidate the maid, in the hope that girl would talk openly, confiding rather than crumbling.

The Queen commenced the proceedings by announcing her disappointment and upset. After such a long and devoted service, she was shocked to uncover a weakness in the girl. She inquired whether Winona had a particular reason for taking such a valuable item. Had she thought of the consequences?

Winona responded quietly, in a whisper, her voice shaking. She hadn't considered the potential financial gain that she could have gained from the brooch, but rather had been overcome with her love for animals. The housekeeper chimed in, inquiring whether any other member of staff had put her up to it. There was a welcome relief from both ladies when the opposite was confirmed.

The housekeeper was taken aback when, early in the proceedings, Catherine announced she had no intention of dismissing Winona from her position. She believed the role would lead to better things for the young girl. The lady in waiting admired the Queen's compassion, which was putting the scullery maid at ease.

The essential punishment was now for the King to decide. She reassured the girl of her support, but still stressed that she must support her husband's judgement. The matter couldn't be trivialised; an adult in the service of the Crown would have spent many years behind bars for the offence. The Queen announced that she intended to set up a meeting at dawn on the balcony, for Winona to stand before the King and hear his judgement. She requested that the lady in waiting and the housekeeper also be in attendance.

The trial on the balcony was scheduled for Sunday. Henry wasn't thrilled to have been woken at such an early hour, especially as he didn't deem the matter worth his time. He walked to the French windows, peering between the heavy curtains. The sun hadn't made an appearance for days, but it seemed today was an exception. The curtains were tied back by the pages. As the drapes parted, Henry spotted Roux outside on the balcony. A promising start to the morning.

The squirrel sat motionless on the corner of the parapet, enjoying the warmer-than-usual start to the morning. The page handed the silver salver to the King as he squeezed through on to the balcony. Roux didn't move or acknowledge his friend; his focus was pinned to the delightful offerings.

For some reason, Roux instinctively felt that he was supposed to be there, but he knew not why. It was just one of his feelings. He felt someone had summoned him to the balcony to take part in something, as though his presence was required. The King sat at the table, the silver salver in front of him, looking forward to the spectacle that was Roux. He never disappointed, separating the nuts from the seeds, the acorns from the chestnuts, selecting some pinecones for good measure. He set aside the items that were going to need transporting to the Oak.

It seemed to Roux that the King was more settled than usual. He was unusually relaxed, as if he wasn't going anywhere in a hurry. Peculiar behaviour, even on the Sabbath. Roux had been hoping to depart promptly. He juggled with a couple of acorns, some seeds and a chestnut, ready to set off home when he was interrupted by the Queen, who joined them on the balcony.

She sat with Henry at the table, pleased to see that he had been entertained by Roux. This always put him in a good mood. Catherine talked with Henry prior to the meeting, giving the young scullery maid an otherwise glowing reference, without downplaying the severity of the crime.

Roux was taken by surprise as two more women entered onto the balcony. He dropped his goods, setting them aside for later, and leaped onto the ivy for cover. When he looked at the women, he recognised the younger of the two. It was the very girl who, for so long, he had wanted to meet. His personal chef, the one who guarantees him his first meal of the day. She took such care, lovingly preparing the silver salver every morning and receiving no thanks for it, something Roux had always wanted to rectify.

The makeshift court was now set up. The two ladies sat in chairs in the corner of the balcony, leaving the young scullery maid standing in the centre. Catherine leant forward, placing the squirrel brooch in the middle of the table. The girl dropped her head in shame at the very sight of it.

Roux stayed hidden in the branches of the ivy, out of sight, but close enough to see the girl's face.

He looked on intently, trying to decipher what was going on.

The housekeeper was asked by the Queen to act as a character witness. She accounted for the young girl's work ethic; always willing to assist, no request was too much trouble. As the scullery maid didn't live in the Palace, she had few friends, but was nonetheless a positive presence in the workforce. Winona was praised for the long hours she put in, her high standard of work. Prior to this incident, she had been considered for promotion. The young girl had recently expressed a desire to read and was wanting to learn. All of which made this lapse a disappointment – a blemish on a promising start. The lady in waiting corroborated with the housekeeper's assessment.

Catherine glanced over to the King, who had now spotted Roux in hiding, overlooking the proceedings. The Queen addressed the balcony as if in court, maintaining her stature. She picked up the brooch, holding it firmly in her hand, demonstrating to her husband how fond of it she was. On behalf of the scullery maid, Catherine asked for clemency. She requested that the King allow her to take on the girl in her personal service, and that she be allowed to visit Winona's family at their home to explain the outcome. She would ask them to spend more time in teaching, espousing a discipline in her home life to prepare her for adulthood.

Before Henry could praise his wife for her benevolence, he noticed Roux in the corner of his eye. The squirrel was climbing down the ivy, slowly, crawling closer to the proceedings. It was as though he was invested in the outcome of the trial. Henry addressed the girl directly but could hardly take his eyes off Roux.

The squirrel was on the parapet now, his focus firmly set on the young girl's countenance. Roux was mesmerised by this small person who had done so much for him. He didn't know how to express his gratitude, but he wanted the King to know how he felt about the proceedings. He jumped on the table, timidly making his way to Winona, climbing up her overalls and settling calmy on her shoulder. The young girl stood absolutely still, the women staring on in disbelief.

With tears in her eyes, The Queen pressed the brooch firmly into the girl's hands – a gesture of understanding. Winona was then subject to the wrath of the King as he slammed his fist down onto the table. Roux gripped the girl's overalls, clinging on tightly to show his allegiance. Catherine raised her hands to Henry, uttering something in Spanish. The King's faced relaxed, the grip of his fist loosening. She had clearly said something to calm him down.

When Roux finally left Winona's shoulder, he left behind a small clump of his red overcoat. Catherine wiped her eyes, explaining to a confused Winona that he wanted her to have a memento and she should place it in the back of the brooch.

"Be thankful that the King has allowed you to continue your young life uninterrupted", Catherine said sternly.

Chapter Three

The Childhood Palace

For Prince Arthur, Princess Mary and the nine-year-old Prince Henry, Eltham Palace was the summer residence they all waited patiently to visit.

Henry is drawn back in time to recall his early years at Eltham. Joyous times spent with his elder brother and younger sister. Every afternoon they would play in the grounds within the walls, facing the parklands where the deer were plentiful, and the hunts were frequent. Those few hours before dusk became mundane, keeping routines of work and protocol in oversized rooms with adjoining halls. They were constantly expected to be on their best behaviour. But in the open air, they could be children again. They stole these fleeting moments out on the grounds, treasuring the normality.

Prince Arthur was an ailing child. His physical abilities didn't match those of his two siblings. He spent his time locked away in bedrooms, far away in the top of the palace, with nursing staff and private tutors who saw to it that he received the necessary education for what should be his future as heir to the throne.

His sister, Mary Tudor, was regarded by family as the intellect. Pleasing to look at and always prepared for discussions far beyond her years, those in her company believed her to be a scholar in the making. She would often take time out to climb the stairs and spend valuable time with Arthur. Then came young Prince Henry. At nine-years-old, he was the child everyone wished to be in the company of. He already had a regal air about him, winning over all those who worried about Arthur's ability to rule in ill-health.

Eltham Palace was blessed with much to wonder at, from the enclosed gardens to the running river, in keeping with a moat surrounding the palace. The children were not allowed to play outside the walls. Venturing beyond the permitted grounds would find them in the depths of the parklands and witness to hunts. It wasn't deemed a suitable pastime for the children. Arthur and Mary would always abide by the restrictions; rules were in place for their own safety. But Prince Henry couldn't accept these draconian measures. In his newfound masculinity, athletic prowess was fast becoming his trademark. The grounds were rich in trees, from elm to chestnut, pines to willows. Henry enjoyed climbing them all to the summit, on the condition that the head gardener was present to oversee the exercise. His spiritedness prompted concern for Arthur by those in power. Unlike his younger brother, the heir couldn't associate himself with such sports.

Henry's philosophy was that the obstacle was there to be conquered. His antics fed his egotism. He was admired for his endurance, having suffered several injuries from some overambitious adventures. Men twice his age would struggle to bounce back, but Henry took the blunders in his stride, never a word of complaint.

The elm was the biggest tree in the grounds, close to the palace wall. Henry had, for some time, wanted to scale the heights of this noble aged tree. He made numerous attempts, only ever managing to climb halfway up through the branches. Chaperones looked on anxiously from below, suggesting he go no further. An accident could well have meant the loss of a much sought-after member of the Royal family.

******

Now in springtime, with the Royal Oak in front of him in Hampton Court, Henry is flooded with memories of his past. He spent some time thinking of his older brother. His untimely passing as a young teenager had inflicted a great sadness onto the young King. It took a considerable time to heal from the grief.

He cast his mind back. He could see Arthur standing at the base of the elm as he disappeared out of sight amongst the foliage. The gardener had just returned from a break that he was forbidden to take until the Prince was safely back on the ground. Arthur wanting desperately to inform his mother of the offence, but his younger brother had convinced him to stay quiet. After all, he may need to call on the gardener for a favour one day.

He remembered, all those years ago now, how he had ordered Arthur to gather wood, suggesting he take the remnants of the wooden bridge, built some months beforehand to allow access to the palace across the river.

With Arthur's help, he tied a hemp cord around his waist and climbed to the top of the elm tree. He pulled himself up, finally, to the heights of the tree and perched on its top branches, sending the cord back down to his brother waiting at the base. Arthur attached the cord to the planks of wood he'd fetched, ready to be hoisted up.

Henry had found a ledge up high, sturdy enough to build his small platform. The work spanned the whole evening, until the palace staff were alerted that the children were outside unsupervised. The staff hurried to the grounds to herd the children indoors, putting an end to the then prince's masterpiece. One day, he swore he would materialise his wish – an observation platform at the very top of the tree with a panoramic view. A world away from all else.

It seemed to him now that this could be the time to bring his project to life. The idea had been stirring since his first meeting with Roux.

In the sunshine with his paint and equipment, the King set about creating a blueprint for his architectural design. A treehouse in the Royal Oak, not just an observation platform, but a means to enjoy life alongside his newfound companion. He wanted to understand Roux and his way of life, how he fended for himself in a world that was home to so many predators.

He had accounted for everything in his plans. The strength of the tree, durability through any type of weather. All that was left was to find the builders, experts to assist him in making the Royal Oak Treehouse a reality, or as Henry endearingly named it, Roux's Country Residence.

The King would need an engineering brain to plot a crossing from the oak tree to the balcony. A walkway, similar to the wooden bridge from which his brother had assisted him in collecting the wood for their first endeavour. He would name the walkway in his brother Arthur's memory. Henry found his engineer but had now ran into a dilemma.

His page entered, announcing that the King's falconer was waiting in the secret garden for a lesson. Falconry, "the sport of kings", was an immense pleasure for Henry, conveying a strong public image that could only be attributed to a natural leader. It became known that the young King wasn't participating in falconry but was overseeing the taming and flying of the birds.

Henry marvelled when he had the hooded bird on his gloved hand, anxious to be set free to fly. He had two hawks and a falcon, and would let them fly and return, keeping a small rodent on his glove as a reward for them, a pride of their obedience. Nonetheless, Henry was conscious that left to their own devices, their prey would consist of whatever small living thing they could get their claws on. Mice, voles, small rabbits, and more often than not, squirrels.

This concerned the King. He couldn't endanger his dear friend, the sole reason for this project, for the sake of sport. He spoke once more with his engineer, ordered the project plans change. The walkway would now be covered, so the traveller could cross with no risk to his life.

His next concern for the treehouse was whether Roux would stick around. The noise and upheaval of the construction could frighten him, causing him to settle elsewhere, never to return. It

would disturb all sense of tranquillity that had
been established since he discovered the place.
The King, keeping faith, ordered the project to go
ahead.

Chapter Four

Regent

The departure of the King of England following a difference of opinion with France bought with it the decision for Henry to inaugurate Catherine as his Regent for the duration of the French battle. An honest act of faith, showing the trust he held in his young bride. In her duties, she would be expected to deal with matters of state, including the impending Battle of Flodden, of which a victory was of paramount importance to the Tudor dynasty.

The Queen now had the task of demonstrating to a sceptical court of advisers and lords that she had the capability and that the King's faith was not misplaced.

It didn't take long for Catherine to show that she was the right choice, her regency was proving an enormous asset to the Tudors. Shortly after her husband's departure, her strategy and planning led to the victory of the Battle of Flodden. She was immediately raised to a higher echelon, people now taking notice of what she had to say. They applauded her strength of character, her patience and compassion. She struggled with statements and speeches, having been unable to master the

English language, but this put no blemish on her record.

The lady in waiting had, this morning, laid out the clothes for the long day ahead. Catherine's itinerary was filled with important negotiations and receptions following her mammoth victory at Flodden. The court was not accustomed to celebrating a victory led by a woman. They planned a function for all to enjoy, as her majesty was keen to repay her subjects for their hard work and loyalty.

There was a certain amount of relief from the powers that be that Catherine had been successful in her husband's absence, but kept talks of the victory to a minimum, as the French siege had not gone to plan. The Queen placed the King at the forefront of her achievement, publicly acknowledging him to be the conquering hero, merely assisted by his regent.

Before the King left for foreign shores, Catherine had assured him she would personally see to it that the silver salver was put out every morning at dawn, setting it down herself.

Over the last month, Roux had adjusted to Henry's absence. His salver hadn't always been in the right place at the right time, but there was enough excellent food to satisfy him. Still, he was longing to know where his red headed friend had gone. Despite her efforts and charm, the Queen lacked her husband's character.

The lady in waiting put the finishing touches to her majesty's ensemble. She stood back, admiring her work. Catherine looked striking, resplendent in all her royal regalia, a wonderful satin dress accented with lace and silk and covered by an ermine cloak resting across her shoulders. Her hair was dressed up, pinned down by a tiara, something rarely worn by the Queen but was now essential as she was representing the crown alone.

They were leaving shortly from the Hampton Court Moorings, due to set off in the royal barge when the morning mist subdued. It would take them an hour and a half to reach Westminster, depending on the tide and the tail wind.

Catherine, now ready to depart, catches sight of the silver salver, sat empty on the dressing table. She urged the lady in waiting to rush down to the kitchen to replenish the offerings, so she can keep her daily promise to the King. She was disappointed to have not witnessed Roux since her husband's departure but put this down to diet. Perhaps if she changed his menu, he might investigate. This morning, she has gone to great lengths to prepare for Roux a typical Spanish banquet, consisting of Saville oranges, grapes, and olives, mixed with his usual assortment of seeds, nuts and acorns. She even left a dash of red wine in his receptacle, in the hope that it assists him through the day.

The lady in waiting returns completely out of breath, carrying the goods on the salver. Catherine beckons for the dish, moving towards the French window. Her lady in waiting insists that she could do this on the Queen's behalf, with her being ready for duties, but Catherine waves her away, passing through the narrow window and stepping out onto the balcony. The lady in waiting watches anxiously, concerned that her majesty could rip her garments, or spill the wine. The manoeuvre was successful, the Queen stands still with her back against the window. Facing her on the parapet is Roux, stood upright, awaiting the salver. She breathes slowly, conscious of her movements. She had learnt from Henry how to best act in Roux's presence, staying still for some minutes. Finally, she seats herself at the table, placing the salver in front of her. Roux takes this as his cue, dashing up the ivy and creeping along the wall. He settles behind the Queen, with an aerial view of the salver, curious as to the change in ingredients.

"The Captain of the Royal Barge says it is time to catch the tide and head for Westminster" urges the lady in waiting.

Catherine is in two minds, deciding that Roux may just need some time to accustom himself to the new breakfast. She will return in the evening to see which of the offerings he takes and which he leaves behind. The Queen leaves his sanctuary, but he is still not convinced. He plans to take with him a small piece of orange a grape, struggling to grip onto them both.

On her way to the barge, Catherine thinks aloud to her lady in waiting. She feels perhaps the formality of her attire may have been off-putting for the young squirrel.

As the oarsman row along the Thames, Catherine cannot stop thinking of the wondrous sight on the balcony. At last she would be able to relay to Henry that they have finally met. She was distracted from the day's tasks, thinking instead ahead to the evening. What could she wear to entice the squirrel to return? And to accept her as a normal person, not the Queen of England? She reflects on the bond between her husband and Roux. Perhaps she ought to dress in night attire, to prove to the little man that she too has to go to bed and sleep from time to time.

As the barge docks at the Tower of London and the oars go up, she instructs her lady in waiting to make sure her wonderful squirrel broach is put out for her to wear this evening on the balcony. A celebratory gesture, both for their encounter and the safe return of the King, for which they were both hoping.

After a full day, the twelve oarsmen prepare to lower their oars to the Thame. The Queen settles under the canopy in the King's comfortable chair as they push away from the side to the middle of the Thames, away from Westminster. Catherine has had a tiring day of official business. She handles all well but is nonetheless weary. The oarsmen find the cool of the evening some help, moving at a good pace with no swell to bother them. They are determined to make good time. Unlike other members of Henry's family, Catherine converses with the rowers, though her broken English limits her ability to do so.

Arriving at Hampton Court, the Queen thanks the men for their valiant effort and the comfortable journey. The lady in waiting assists the Queen in alighting the barge, and together they take a short walk around the gardens.

As the two women reach the private apartments, word is sent to the kitchen that her majesty is back and will shortly be ready for her meal. Her evening attire is laid over the bed, she has the choice of either evening casualwear to dine, or her night attire for comfort.

Her remaining duties for the day take priority to her much-thought-about encounter on the balcony. She opts for casualwear. Opening the window and feeling the chill, she decides to wrap Henry's beloved deerskin rug around her shoulders, believing that it might help in her introduction to dinner with her newfound friend. She sits silently, patiently, in the chair. She looks over to the silver salver. The nuts, seeds and acorns had all been taken, along with some orange and grape.

The Ivy rustles on the wall behind her. Catherine spots Roux on his downward path, nearing the table. He darts from branch to branch, making the Queen quite dizzy in trying to follow his every move.

Catherine finds herself relaxing quietly, letting the squirrel entertain her with his tour de force. Roux eventually calms down, having recognised a look of joy on the Queen's face. He can tell she enjoys his company and approaches her on the table, performing comical poses to make her laugh. This manner of encounter might have to be kept from Henry, as it may bring out his jealous side.

Roux is with Catherine for a long while, moving closer with time. Eventually, her majesty extends a hand of friendship, placing her hand palm-up on the table, unsure of what reaction this could bring.

Roux steps forwards, sitting himself on the palm of her hand. She gently places an acorn near him for him to try. He takes it with both paws, demonstrating how they open. Catherine addresses him for the first time in Spanish. The squirrel doesn't understand, looking up at her inquisitively. She keeps talking as he rests in her hand, bringing her other hand closer, slowly, she begins to stroke her new friend down his back. The Queen feels as though she is dreaming. How she wishes Henry could see. She sings the young squirrel a lullaby in her native tongue.

It was evident that Roux was perhaps not so keen on orange and grape. The Queen made sure that they wouldn't feature on the salver again.

It took Roux several journeys to carry all of his food home. Catherine sat at the table still, basking in the relaxation of the evening. Roux returned for the final time, having successfully delivered all his goods back to the Royal Oak. He wiped both his eyes, indicating it was time to retire for the night. Her majesty returned the gesture, announcing that she intended to do the same.

The two wished each other good night, both hoping to resume their time together very soon.

Chapter Five

Love Knots

Roux was unaware of the turmoil Henry was going to impose on his life.

Roux had taken a month's break to look to his home and plan any alterations. He considered what he could do to give the oak a more romantic feel, in the hope of interesting a potential partner. It was summer now, the right time for finding a mate.

The young squirrel had filled the larder to the brim, demonstrating a willingness to gather harvest. He knew he had an advantageous location, but he was also aware that his décor was perhaps not to everyone's taste. There was much to ponder over, but he felt an urgent need to get out there. The loneliness he felt made him feel hollow, he was yearning for family.

He had always heeded his mother's advice which was revered in squirrel society. She lived her life well, having spent her three-year life expectancy happily with his father. The changes she had made to their home were only put in place on the arrival of their children.

Having had two girls and one boy, she had to focus on the two girls, while Roux's father concentrated on him, a much greater responsibility. Roux had to be taught how to evade danger, be that predators, troublesome areas and quarrels with his own kind. He had to guard his collection of food that he'd buried, only letting his mother or father know its whereabouts. Roux had always thought he would pass the same teachings onto his children if he were blessed with the opportunity.

Finally came the choice which was, as his mother had explained, a choice that nobody could help him with. A scent, a glance, maybe a chase. Whatever he did, he had to get the attention of a chosen beauty. His big card was his property. He prepared himself for the most important moment of his life, unaware that Henry would soon throw his life into disarray, undoing all the work he had undertaken to impress his future partner in life.

Roux recalled a conversation with his father, where he had been advised that the evening was best for meeting a mate. He decided that he would cross over to the balcony for his meal before setting out on his pursuit.

It was a pleasant evening, but the King was not in residence. Still, Winona had left the sumptuous silver salver. He savoured the offerings before setting off on his journey into the park, which he knew was home to different families of squirrels.

Roux wasn't, at this moment, sure if he should mention his private affairs with the King. He wasn't sure if advertising his royal ties would help or hinder him in his search for a partner. He didn't want to appear arrogant. What if his new love wasn't a royalist? No, he wouldn't mention it at first. Roux thought it best to perhaps keep it up his sleeve, choosing his moments wisely. The balcony and its occupants might offer or induce a feeling of grandeur if he needed.

He ambled rather nervously into the wooded area, sitting himself under a pine to collect himself and scope the place out. He didn't want to jump into anything at the risk of chasing the wrong mate, or worse putting someone off. There's nothing worse than an overly keen show-off, after all. He needed an approach that would exhibit his charm.

Many people, like the King and Queen, had remarked on his impressive plume. The white flash made Roux stand out, and so he stood beneath the pine, perfecting the angle of his tail. He gave it a good spruce, making sure it hung over his head for all to see. Still, he lacked confidence. Tail in place and with acorns around him to demonstrate his gathering ability to impress or perhaps entice if the opponent has not found what she wanted on her evening stroll; Roux waited

He could hear rustling overhead, drawing closer , a feeling that someone was focused on him just a few yards away but with squirrels always being able to use their finest attributes of camouflage with the silence came the scent ,and recognisable sounds, Things were building and Roux was exhibiting signs of excitement and expectancy as Down from the pine scurried a beautiful young squirrel. The atmosphere was veering towards an unknown anticipation, she eventually calmed down having burnt off a considerable amount of excess energy which seemingly had little effect on Roux who remained motionless, In her eyes he was probably playing hard to get. A different tactic was required as she had to quickly get his attention somehow before he tired and left for pastures new, she came down the tree slowly, determined with a more distinctive slinky feel in her approach now presenting a more sensual side to her nature with apparently the desired effect as it would appear at last, it seems that she knew what she was doing more importantly to him what she wanted. Roux had a nervous energy. He stood still, holding his stance, allowing the female to show herself off. Finally, after more devious endeavours for his attention she makes it quite clear that she wants to look him up and down, a thorough investigation proceeds to quantify his appearance, his capabilities as there were matters of more importance to confirm,

Her efforts seemed fruitless as Roux was remaining motionless. She tried a different tactic to gain his attention, moving shyly as she approached him.

Facing each other, the two squirrels examined their prospective partners. The young female seemed satisfied with Roux, and he too was impressed. There was no questioning her beauty. A full, rustic coat with no blemishes, nut brown eyes, cute ear tufts. There was a chemistry between them. She needed now a definite proposal, and Roux was happy to take her home. On arrival at the Royal Oak, the reaction was just as he had hoped, and no one had turned up to put forward any valid reason why they couldn't go ahead. There was no way that this lady would consider any other suitor, not when she could live a life in this stately home. Roux now took the opportunity of giving her the name, Beatrix . There was just one thing she hadn't mentioned to Roux, and she was avoiding the matter at the risk of losing him. She was with kitten, and she didn't know how to tell him.

Admitting such a thing would be difficult for anyone. So far, Roux hadn't put a foot wrong. With each passing day she grew fonder of him, but he still didn't know about her kitten. It wouldn't be long now until her pregnancy starts to show, and Roux would certainly put two and two together.

Beatrix had cooked the best meals, collected his favourite foods, allowed him time for balcony meetings without complaint, but still she felt that divulging her secret could lead to their divorce.

One evening when Roux had returned from the balcony with an unusually fulsome picnic, courtesy of the King, and laid it out on their dining room table, Beatrix decided that would be the course to follow their supper.

Frightened of the outcome, Beatrix confronted the situation, telling Roux the truth about her kitten through tears. Roux listened carefully, although he didn't like what he was hearing.

By now, they were very much in love, and Roux had been raised well, instilled with a calm, understanding nature. He told his beloved that he was honoured to have the opportunity of raising a kitten. He would see to it that this young kitten felt at home in the Royal Oak. Beatrix gasped, endlessly grateful for Roux's compassion. She knew then that their union was safe.

The walkway was the monarch's pièce de résistance, his first step to launching his Treehouse. He had spent many late hours hunched over candlelight, drawing up plans. The builders were carefully chosen on the basis of their previous works.

Two weeks earlier, Henry had ridden twelve miles to Eltham Palace to meet with the head gardener and his architects. They had spent considerable time researching the layout and measuring everything to replicate the same features back at Hampton Court. Henry was striving for accuracy, so as to honour the memory of Arthur.

The King put the finishing touches to his visualisation of how it would look in Hampton Court, noting all of its intricate details. The interwoven timbers for banisters, the plaited safety barriers, ornate posts, even the emblems on the arrival gates of Greenwich Palace. He had done a remarkable job.

On his return to Hampton Court, Henry ordered a further elm to be felled, as it was needed to make two more support beams, of which there were already ready eight, standing over thirty-five feet tall. They hadn't been essential, but the King insisted on their presence with them having such prominence at Eltham. The walkway itself measured sixty-five feet in length and would be placed at the back of the oak, well away from Roux's main entrance.

Henry was keen to build the walkway before all else was considered. He felt that if all went well and Roux didn't vacate the property out of fear, then the young squirrel would be more prepared for the further stages of construction, which would cause much more disruption.

Henry hoped that Roux would use the walkway on a regular basis. The King would extend the offer of kitchen fruit scraps, accumulated by Winona, more liberally, hoping it would entice the young squirrel to cross the walkway more often, bringing the three of them together for some quality time.

Henry decided to let his Queen in on his secret plans, provided that she swore to secrecy. Any slip of the tongue would be severely dealt with. Well aware of Henry's temper, Catherine knew exactly what that meant. It was for that reason that she chose to not tell the King of her encounters with Roux. When aggravated, his rage knew no bounds.

Henry was pleased with Catherine's involvement in the friendship. She brought to the regal trio an invaluable maternal instinct, little touches of thought that otherwise wouldn't be considered, like a receptacle of water beside the silver salver, always filled with fresh water.

In the courtyard alongside the Coach House, the wood supports were all ready to be put in place. The project was now on its way. Those passing, rubbernecking at the construction, were warned off. It's just a busy time for renovations, they were told. A sign was pinned to the door, indicating that what lay beyond was a private royal matter, and that any interference would be grounds for persecution by the King.

The supports were erected at night, when nobody was around. The walkway, with all its intricacies, had taken over two months to build, and was now ready to be fitted. It had been decided by his majesty that the walkway would no longer have a roof, contrary to his original plans, deciding that he better give Roux some freedom.

The walkway was spectacular. Despite having spent way beyond his budget, Harry was overjoyed. It was admired by all as a display of the King's architectural skills. Catherine had decked the bannisters with wildflowers from the Eltham's riverbank, in memory of Arthur, a gentle gesture appreciated by her husband.

An architectural success, but the very reason for it being built wasn't happening. It had been nearly eight days and the walkway hadn't been used. The King supposed, hoped even, that Roux was merely keeping his head down, shying from the noise of the carpentry. But was he still here? The monarch was not impressed with Roux's delay, having invested a great deal of his time and money in the crossing.

Catherine tried to pacify the King, encouraging patience. After all, the situation was in the hands of an animal, who no one could as yet understand.

"Some things are worth waiting for", uttered Catherine. That old adage. It had little success with Henry, who felt for the first time during his reign that he had been ignored. He would have certainly never accepted this from a person, not without fatal consequence.

One early evening, as the monarchs were enjoying a summer evening on their balcony, they could hear a gentle tapping coming from the walkway. Henry and Catherine shared a glance, hopeful that it was Roux's paws they were hearing as he scurries along the wood. They stood up swiftly, peering down the walkway. Whatever it was had lost its nerve at their sudden movement, scuppering back the way it came.

Henry took on Catherine's advice to practice patience. An hour or so later, they were once again alerted movement on the walkway, again making its way towards the royal couple. Its footing giving an air of confidence this time. The couple remained totally still, not wanting to repeat their hastiness. To the King and Queen's delight, there appeared Roux, in all his splendour.

Catherine kept up her secret, acting as though she had never before met the King's little friend. She was mesmerised by his beauty. The plume that Henry had so often described looked better than ever, complimented by the light of the evening sun.

The evening took a turn, when Roux walked forwards beside another young squirrel, proudly introducing the King and Queen to his wife, who, it appeared, was the reason for the first retreat, getting cold feet at the last minute.

******

Roux takes advantage of the unfinished part of the walkway when he sets off on his outings in search of food. As yet, he hasn't been accompanied by Beatrix. It was risky at this stage in her pregnancy for her to venture out in the dark. She is, however, grateful for the showering of food and attention from Roux, and in turn tries to keep a clean home, working hard alongside Roux on the upper floors.

The exterior of the tree is once again being ransacked, the builders reaching a crescendo of noise, disturbing the squirrels in their home. Beatrix found the interference unacceptable, taking to her usual corner of the hall and curling up tight. Roux is away on one of his expeditions, though Beatrix doesn't know where. All she knows is that he wanders for some time, in the hope of stumbling across suitable food. He doesn't venture too far out, conscious that in his wife's condition, she may need him at any time.

The builders have had to take drastic measures to strengthen the supports for the walkway, chopping into the oak in doing so, destroying the main entrance to the tree. Beatrix shifts anxiously on her paws. She's terrified. She doesn't know what to do or how to cope with the wounds being inflicted on her home.

The noise is more than she can bear. She starts to scrabble up to the higher floors, trying to distance herself from the chaos. Scaling the walls, Beatrix loses her footing, falling straight down to the base of the tree. She lay there for some time, face down, showing no sign of life.

It is nearly an hour before Roux arrives home, having failed to source their food. He notices the builders at work and the destruction they're causing. Noticing that his main entrance has been demolished, he climbs the exterior of the oak.

Roux gets through and climbs down to the basement. He spots Beatrix, lying there covered in sawdust and bark. Cavities were now visible on both sides of the trunk. He races forwards, clearing the debris from her back and turning her over. He hunches himself over her, desperately looking for some sign of life. Time moved slowly then, but finally he noticed Beatrix breathing a soft breath. He pulls her away from the working areas, noticing blood where she had been lying. The fall had surely affected her pregnancy. Roux expected that they had lost their kitten. Still, Roux had to prioritise Beatrix's life, getting his love to safety. He took her aside, making her comfortable with leaves and fern.

He spends the entire night on a nervous vigil, urging Beatrix to drink water, lying closely at her side. Morning seeming an eternity away.

******

Beatrix recovered, not overnight, but soon enough, with Roux's aid and twenty-four-hour nursing. She needed to recover both physically and mentally having to come to terms with her accident. She had lost her kitten. The home she shared so lovingly with Roux no longer held the same warmth, its memories tied to preparations of parenthood. The tree would, for the first time, feel hollow. She longed for a new life, a new home. Roux understood but struggled to support her wishes. He had spent so much of his short life within the Royal Oak, he couldn't just leave. But equally, he couldn't abandon his love, who meant more to him than the tree ever could.

Catherine thought of the superstition, the folklore, of which people talked so endearingly. It was often said that his majesty's red hair, matching her own, brought great luck and fortune to the throne. Sadly, such speculations were just that. Catherine lost her first child; her daughter was stillborn. Henry was shaken by the loss of his baby daughter. He had, of course, always hoped for a son, but his reservations seemed trivial now. For now, he felt a deep sorrow for his wife. The King was not reserved in announcing the passing of his child.

Apart from Roux, no one knew of Beatrix's misfortune. They had kept their matters private, hoping, in time, to try for their own kitten.

In Hampton Court, Henry had reached the same decision. It was no good to keep on grieving for the stillborn child. She would never be forgotten, but they had to move forwards. He hoped it would not be too long before he and his Queen could try for another child, something the nation looked forward to.

Chapter Six

The Father of the Royal Navy

Early morning in the Palace grounds, it was a damp and murky start. A distant sound of marching could be heard from the gardens on the east of the estate. The marching grew clearer, still a fair distance away, but approaching at pace.

These two figures were now just distinguishable, the gravel crunching under their feet as they materialised through the lifting blanket of morning fog. They are to present themselves to the King of England, their new commander in chief. The young King had founded the remarkable armed force himself, giving him the revered title of The Father of the Royal Navy. He has summoned members of his elite force to join him in the construction of his special project.

The sound of the crunching gravel was now attracting the attention of the gardeners and staff, who are going about their early duties. The two men in their stride reach the fountain, having walked over two miles down the bridle paths, entering the estate from the east end and heading straight in the direction of the gatehouse, the entrance to their destination.

The two men were of different rank, apparent as the taller of the two was attired in officers' uniform – a blue tailcoat decorated with gold braid, white breeches and tights, and buckled shoes. The other uniformed member sported a shorter jacket with long grey trousers, a yellow waistcoat, and a black scarf around his neck, finished with a blue peaked cap – that of a subordinate or a sailor.

Six sailors followed behind them, carrying a large amount of hemp rope on a gun carriage, finding the weight testing. Two lengths of thirty-five feet of twisted hemp had been ordered, making the strongest rope that could be found anywhere in the world. It had been twisted especially in accordance with Henry's wishes by members of the Royal Navy's Chatham Ropery. Lying on top of the rope is fifty wooden slats, necessary for the rope ladders.

They arrived exactly on time as the gatehouse clock announced the seventh hour, as requested by the monarch. He had, one month earlier, chosen the two men and the sailors for this particular task. It wasn't until he had visited both Portsmouth and Chatham that he saw for himself the masterful work. He saw their rope ladders lashed to the decks, leading all the way up to the foreboding crows' nests. Nobody else could match the work of these men, Henry had decided.

The weather was a concern. The drizzling morning meant the base of the oak would have a slippery surface, making for a hazardous first climb, particularly while carrying the heavy rope.

Portsmouth and Chatham sailors were put to task. The monarch had given stringent orders, etched in blood, stating clearly that the tree is to remain untouched. The sailors were not to use any intrusive materials, no nails, nothing of the sort. He stressed the importance of damage limitation, necessary for safeguarding the Royal Oak and its inhabitants. The last thing he wanted was to frighten Roux and Beatrix off.

The men worked hard in the damp conditions, adhering as best they could to the King's requests. The result was amazing, the tree unscathed by the latest bout of construction. The first twenty-five feet of the ladder was installed by draping the hemp over a larger branch, its durability tested by three sailors hanging on the rope to see if it could take their weight. The first section of ladder was supported by two elm beams, stretching from floor to branch. The beams took the strain, allowing the ladder to hang a foot and a half from the tree's trunk, leaving ample room for a good foothold.

The rope was glued with a resin base for safety and strength, still allowing for some sway.

At the top of the first ladder, a four-foot platform was hauled up by three sailors, pieced together as a rest area, for climbers to take a brief break before attempting the second flight. It took two days for the ladders to be installed; the navy's job was now finished, and the work of the treehouse would now be transferred to the carpenters.

The carpenters were now in a position to use the ladders, using them to pass materials and tools from the ground to the tops of the tree. The ground had already been laid, making it possible now for them to start work on the walls.

Henry, always keen to be suitably attired, gave his tailor the task of devising a costume of a thick, olive green material, designed by the King himself to celebrate the completion of his treehouse. He wanted the Queen to be dressed in similar attire, ordering that both ensembles be suitable for climbing.

For Catherine's birthday, Henry presented her with a replica of his squirrel brooch, replacing the one that she had so generously gifted to the scullery maid some time ago. He attached his own brooch to his new autumnal regalia, and suggested the Queen do the same, ready for the launch of their latest project.

The house was completed in two weeks, with two charming leaded windows, a chimney stack able to direct smoke from a small fire grate upwards into the clouds, table and chairs, and, in the corner, a chaise longue for the Queen which was a present from the King of France which Henry had not known what to do with but which fitted perfectly in the surroundings. In one corner shelving to take a small but efficient larder of snacks for himself and his Regent along with close friends and guests which he had given much thought to, the finishing touch was for the door by placing an immensely ornate emblem proudly depicting the Navy, honouring the men who had so valiantly worked to create his dream and make it come true with good will and loyalty.

Chapter Seven

The Stairway to Heaven

Roux had not been officially informed of his imminent elevation into squirrel society. His instinct told him something was a foot, That he must be aware of a forth coming announcement of some importance, which, could be life changing requiring him to act in a more positive and responsible fashion but, as yet the expectation is not being shared with him.

There was no doubt that Beatrix was acting strangely. She was cleaning manically, clearly unsettled. Not a day passed without her carrying out her rigorous schedule, clearing the lower end of the oak. She was sleeping more than usual, retreating to her bed in the afternoon. Far different to her typical lifestyle.

Roux said nothing of his love's manic behaviour. He aided her cleaning, finishing off his jobs when satisfied with the results, while Beatrix carried on, clearing dirt and mess that only she could see. She began rearranging the furniture into spaces where they definitely didn't belong. Roux followed, not far behind, shunting everything back to their original places.

The hysterical behaviour reminded him of his mother. When she was carrying Roux's sisters, she had adopted the same frenzy. It was then that the penny finally dropped. He and Beatrix are expecting a kitten of their own. This was news to be shared.

Beatrix was spotted daily, collecting flora and fauna, sometimes fern and bracken leaves, from the gardens to decorate the nursery. Roux thought this excessive, she was bringing in far too much material for their modest requirements. He said nothing, humouring her as she excitedly presented to him her new finds.

In Beatrix's hormonal state, there were times when they both needed space. The new home arrangements didn't allow for it, with any extra space being taken up by articles for the nursery. To give himself some headspace, Roux made the habit of awaking at the crack of down and making a trip across the walkway. The infancy of the day could always put a spring in his step.

Things were changing for the young squirrel. A kitten of his own on its way, he was gaining a whole different outlook on his once mundane life. He was keen to tell his dear friend Henry of the next chapter in his life.

Roux would arrive on the balcony as dawn was breaking. Likewise, Henry would settle in his high-backed chair at the table, his rustic box of letters and scrolls open beside him to be poured over before he commenced his day.

The King rarely looked up from his work, even in the company of Roux. The young squirrel didn't mind, he understood the pressure of his friend's role. These matters had to be tended to. It didn't change how Roux felt about time spent with the King, for whom he still held a great affection. He knew that he too was held in high regard by his friend, conscious that had he not made the journey across the walkway for his nuts and seeds, Henry would surely be disappointed. This daily routine was often what the King arose so early for. Any later in the day would be much too noisy, and Henry didn't want to subject his friend to any more chaos. Catherine had joined them today, on one of her rare occasional visits to the balcony, finding Roux's presence a special one. She sat beside the King, overawed by the dear squirrel.

The rustic box was finally shut, in time for Roux finishing his selection from the salver. He stuffed his cheeks with acorns and parted ways with the royal couple, heading back to his wife, and soon-to-be mother of his kitten.

Catherine had been the first to enquire why Beatrix hadn't been seen lately. She put her concerns to the King, curious if the squirrels had been struck by some unfortunate luck. Henry eased her nerves. He had spotted her recently, standing on the edge of the walkway by the tree trunk, waiting for Roux's return.

******

After a long labour, the young kitten was born a boy. This was great news for his father, now having an heir. The couple would experience the same process several times over the next three years, as Roux and Beatrix have more children. The King and Queen were delighted to have a full family of squirrels in residence. In some ways, they envied them, having not been able to have a child of their own.

One morning, the family of squirrels could hear movement at the base of the tree. A page had been sent up the ladders with a servant carrying a basket of food. They descended the tree and waited at the bottom as the lady in waiting made her way up. She was struggling, her arms were tiring. She stopped at several rungs to compose herself, trying to negotiate her court robes which were by no means designed for this. The ladder had to be trialled before the lady in waiting allowed Catherine to attempt the climb. She rested at the first platform, waiting for her majesty, as she needed to be present for assistance should the Queen need.

Catherine was a little more physically capable than the stout lady in waiting. The Queen, having watched Henry scale the tree on numerous occasions, knew how it should be done. She arrived at the first stage. The lady in waiting gulped, anxious to tackle her next climb – the longer of the two ladders. She hesitated to place her foot on the first rung, only moving when hearing the King bellow from below to get on with it, he didn't have all day. With her majesty close behind, she shimmied up the to the top.

Henry was keen to show off his athletic ability, scaling the ladders in record time. Without stopping for breath, he arrived at the summit.

The King welcomed the ladies to his treehouse, proudly showing off the designs that he himself had drawn. He invited Catherine and her lady to sit, allowing Catherine her first ever experience of the chaise longue, gifted to him by the King of France.

Henry instructed the lady in waiting to set about preparing the afternoon meal. While they waited, he and Catherine sat on the narrow veranda amongst the branches, looking out onto the exquisite view. It was a sunny afternoon. The Queen relished times like these, when the two could detach from their duties. Henry had arranged this visit on a weekend, knowing they had no official matters to see to and so could sit undisturbed.

The royal couple savoured their delicately prepared buffet. They took their time, giving Roux and his family the opportunity to appear. Henry asked for complete quiet during the meal, conscious of the noises travelling through the tree and startling the tenants.

An hour and a half passed before Roux showed his face, appearing having just surfaced from a long sleep. He squeezed out and did his usual tour of the treehouse, scurrying along the branches, putting on a show for their majesties. To the joy of the small audience, Beatrix soon joined, introducing the King and Queen to her new-born son. The boy shuffled on his feet, hiding behind his mum, peering around to look at the royal strangers.

The encounter lasted five minutes. Brief, but long enough to satisfy the royals. It was brought to an end when the baby squirrel tugged at his mum's tail, indicating he wanted to go back inside. With that, the squirrel family retreated.

Chapter Eight

A JOINT CELEBRATION

Late afternoon at Hampton Court Palace, a sense of optimism passes over. The evening approaches, bringing the advent of a perfect red sky, its own royal seal of approval.

For Roux, the red sky felt significant. His instincts were telling him that something out of the ordinary may be occurring very soon in the palace grounds. Earlier that morning on the balcony, the King gave the impression that he was pressed for time, hurriedly looking over only a few letters before he packed up and headed back inside.

Roux spent some time dashing up and down the oak in an attempt to discover the best vantage point, as high as could be. He wanted a good view to see what it was that was going to unfold below. After altercations with intrusive leaves, twigs and branches, he settled for a small join in the crown of the oak. He had wisely assumed it was going to be a long night, bringing with him a few acorns and seeds to last him throughout.

The squirrel was anxious. Three enormous elms had been axed down that morning. A thoughtless gesture, he thought, depriving him and others of both habitat and food. The chopped wood had been transported down to the Thames moorings, placed in several torch beacons along the river's edge. Rarely seen in peacetime, usually only lit as a warning or celebration. He kept his paws crossed for the latter. More beacons lined the gardens and pathways leading to the main entrance, illuminating the carriage drive.

This grand spectacular for which these preparations were being made was a joint celebration of the most recent victories, his Regent's success at the Battle of Flodden and Henry's victory returning from Calais victorious after skirmish with the French. The King's beloved new Navy was going to be the envy of the world. The monarchs were basking in their glory, receiving laudation from the adoring nation.

Two white steeds, gifted from the King of France, were brought out of the Coach House stables to be groomed and plaited, set to carry the King and Queen. Three coaches were brought out into the yards by the King's coachman, prepared to collect family dignitaries. All were being seen to by the royal farrier, whose job hadn't been made easy. The horses had been out at Windsor Great Park, part of long hunt and now in need of urgent attention.

The King could be seen in the courtyard, checking the horses and exercising his two

deerhounds, who seemed well at home amongst
the steeds. He felt fondly of his hounds, having
them sit one either side of him by a roaring
fireplace, adding to his powerful persona. They
were important to him, but to Roux, they were
fearsome creatures with ambition of tearing him to
pieces. He was hardly a sizeable meal; he couldn't
possibly satisfy their appetites.

Catherine was obviously more in command
of the welcoming committee along with her four
housekeepers and hugely respected lady in
waiting. The Queen stood on the lawns,
surrounded as always by her four close friends,
the Duchesses of Cornwall, Essex, Guildford and
Devon, all vying for her attention.

Seeing the preparations going on beneath
him, Roux was glad his only responsibility in life
was to look after his wife and children. He saw the
King and Queen, and how much nonsense they
had to endure. Always putting on a show, never
able to truly relax and be themselves.

The red evening sky was turning pink, slowly
being replaced by the dark clouds of night. Roux's
attention was drawn to the French windows above
the gatehouse, opening to reveal four men in
tunics holding horns. He sat bolt upright as the
sound of the horns echoed through the air. He had
never heard anything like it, except the hunting

horn, which could often be heard ringing from the depths of the forests.

The windows closed. Under the arches of the gatehouse, out came twenty-four pages in their red and gold jackets, each carrying a wicker torch. They march to their respective destinations, their footing keeping in time with one another. An awesome sight for the small squirrel to take in.

The first batch of torches are carried down to the palace moorings to be lit, just before the evening light disappears. Flames reflected in the water, transforming the scene of an ordinary riverbank into one of a fairy tale. A royal torch that can be seen a mile down the Thames, for guests to feel that they are indeed arriving into a different world, in the company of the King and Queen of England.

Roux is woken after short nap to the sound of hooves. He wipes his eyes and looks outside. Approaching the palace grounds is the first carriage, pulled by four striking horses thundering into the main courtyard, where the pages, grooms and stable lads are waiting to assist. As the coach wheels come to a halt, the window of the gatehouse opens, the four heralds welcoming the first guests with a fanfare. Having already witnessed the grandiose rehearsals in the afternoon, Roux now enjoys hearing it again.

The carriage footmen open the doors, placing the steps in position for their passengers to alight. They stay to attention until the guests have reached the top of the stairs, where the duchesses take over, meeting them on the veranda to give a special welcome. Many guests arrived on foot, leaving their carriages to enjoy the evening stroll through the immaculate grounds.

It was known by plenty that the last festivity held at Hampton Court involved a seven-hour dinner of twenty courses. The King had extended the merrymaking by a further two hours, wanting to dance until the hall itself was in need of a rest. The staff were struggling to stay awake. It was likely that the guests arriving at the palace were in for a long night.

Roux is tiring of the parade. He's watched over forty coaches make the same entrance, taking over an hour. He had been sat still for some hours now, deciding he was in need of some exercise. Curious as to what was happening in the Great Hall, he thought he would cross the walkway. Hopefully someone might have remembered to leave him his silver salver on the balcony.

Roux took that evening to stroll across the walkway up to the parapets. There it was, his silver salver. Full to the brim with some of the evening's delicacies, things he had never seen before. He couldn't attribute this work to Winona, whoever had assembled it had little understanding of a squirrel's diet. He rummaged through the salver, setting aside the meats and the ferns and leaves, which he wouldn't normally bother with. He heard an eruption of cheering from the Great Hall. Things were getting going. He left the balcony, climbing the ivy to get closer to the noise and settling himself on a vantage point he found in the roof.

The fires were now raging inside, torches hanging around the walls. He climbed higher up the steep outer wall, a dangerous manoeuvre even for Roux. He stopped outside a window with a good view of the celebrations. He stands there mesmerised by the entertainment. Acrobats in the centre of the hall, jugglers using the cutlery as props. He notices an array of food covering the long tables, lining the walls of the hall, understanding now the change in menu on his salver.

In the centre of both tables were elegantly displayed cooked swans, a great favourite of Henry's. Beside them sat two entire boars on long platters, clutching the customary apples, matched by two pigs and some generously stuffed geese. The tables were stacked high. In the fireplace, chickens were hanging, roasting over the flames.

There are fruit aplenty, and fresh vegetables all along the buffet. The serving wenches cannot keep up with the events. They hurry around the hall, pewter in hand, topping up endless empty mugs with ale and mead.

Roux being a keen conservationist was appalled to see just how much timber the banquet had used. Torches, beacons, fires, not to mention the kitchen requirements. Everywhere he looked, timber was set alight. Many trees would have been ravaged for this one night.

He spotted the King amidst the crowd, dancing with young lady courtiers in a bawdy manner, encouraged by the cheering men of the room. Henry was dressed from head to foot in ostentatious gold costume, accompanied by his famous sandals with single bar in gold satin, gold garters flaunting his medals, chains of commendation for bravery and courage hanging around his around his neck. The King certainly looked the part, but to Roux, he wasn't acting like it.

Catherine was sat composed at a table, keeping an eye on her husband. She knew how to bring her husband back to reality should the need occur, making sure she had the duchesses at her side. The night was long, but she was expected to see it through to its end.

The King now in need of a comfort break led the way out into the open courtyard which the pages had prepared for such a need, the royal stable buckets were in a long line down the cobbled alleyway. With the vast consumption of ale the buckets were visibly filled quickly making the pages having to run in and out keeping a supply of empty receptacles for the comfort of the guests, it was however never fortunately disclosed how the ladies took their comfort break with discretion being adhered to.

The uncouthness and disorder that kicked in with the ale was appalling to see. Roux looked on, wondering whether anybody was actually enjoying themselves or if they were merely conforming to royal demands. He was disappointed in his friend Henry. The whole affair seemed a selfish display of self-indulgence.

Roux felt now that he had spent much too long at the window, investing his time in the exhibition of grandeur, which now seemed unworthy of such attention. Perhaps he should concentrate on his own matters, not so eloquent but more in keeping with his lifestyle. He walked home, eager to get back to Beatrix and the kittens.

He reached the comfort of his sanctuary and peered outside of the trunk to watch as drunken dignitaries headed for their coaches, some were even carried, leaving in a far worse state than they had arrived. Roux was finding it hard to find one guest who could walk still walk in a straight line.

The King continued dancing. His guests who would be residing in the palace overnight were now paying the price of the invitation, now realising that they had little chance of ever seeing their beds.

Roux had a lot to think about as he evaluated his relationship with Henry. He was stunned to see how drastically different the King could be in his public persona, compared to the King that he met on the balcony each morning.

******

News had spread that Catherine was now, for the second time in under a year, expecting a child. He was optimistic, not allowing the tragedy of their last child to fester. If Catherine is to have a boy, then Henry will finally have an heir to the throne. Son or daughter, Catherine was elated, knowing that this child would be a favourable addition to the Tudor dynasty.

Henry was now leaving behind the immaturity of his teenage temperament, taking on an adult approach to the difficult decisions he faced each day. He was handling matters constructively, with confidence and authority. Still, there was an uncomfortable malaise emanating from those in power. The King was seldom listening to those around him, setting his judgements and refusing to reconsider. Officials feared that even Thomas Wolsey couldn't rein him in.

Henry's decision to remove the treehouse was made without consultation, the excuse being that not enough guests were enjoying the instalment. He terminated the whole project, angry that his time and effort, the gesture towards his departed brother, had gone unappreciated. Catherine disapproved of the decision, believing once more that he should exercise some patience. She quizzed her husband. Had he not considered the occupants of the tree?

Henry was adamant. The decision was made. He had already had the rope ladders hoisted high up into the apex of the tree so no person nor animal could gain access.

Roux hadn't been across to the balcony for some time. Henry sat alone in the mornings, which The Queen thought unfortunate. A visit from his friend could be all it takes to quash the King's desire to destroy the treehouse. Unbeknown to the royal couple, Roux was taking paternal leave. He and Beatrix had had a son. Roux was spending every spare moment running around to gather the needs and wants of Beatrix and the new kitten.

Autumn was in its infancy. The red evening skies were replaced by heavy clouds, hanging low and moving swiftly, assisted by the strong winds.

Roux, Beatrix and their children were unsure how to tackle the new climate. The coldness outside caught them by surprise. Perhaps it's time for them to retreat to the interior of the oak and settle down some weeks earlier than they had planned.

The change in weather was an annual disappointment to those who took solace in the outdoors. Winter clothing was brought out of hibernation to compensate for the unexpected drop in temperature. Ladies were sporting heavy cloaks, covering layers of heavier dress. Men were noticeably attired in long coats buttoned to the neck.

Roux was unusually nervous. Sounds outside the tree were giving him certain cause for concern. Henry had closed the treehouse, the imminent destruction programme set to take place shortly. There was an eeriness to the air, an unwelcome tranquillity.

Activity at the base of the tree alerted Roux to trouble. There was a threat to his family. He waited for dark before peering out, positioning himself at his vantage point under the stars to see what was happening outside. Things were not normal in the top branches. They were creaking under the weight of the nesting that was being gathered by large, heavy birds. He was concerned for the safety of his family. Predators were seeking a permanent refuge, and they had opted for his oak. It wouldn't be long now until they would be seeking food. He couldn't stomach the thought of moving from his home, but he may not have a choice. Where could they possibly go?

Roux decided to keep the threat to himself for now. Daylight would give him a clearer picture. He would think up a strategy for moving forward, so as to not put Beatrix on the edge of her nerves.

Days later, some of Henry's staff overheard a conversation in court, questioning the validity of the treehouse project. Talks that the King had erected a treehouse in the large, sprawling tree opposite his private apartments for his amusement, to enjoy the company of his squirrel family. Indulging in youthful practices at the expense of important matters of national interest, spoke one gossiper with mirth. The statement swept through the palace. Those who understood Henry's temperament were uneasy, anticipating an eruption at any moment.

Thankfully, his staff of secretaries and notaries were able to keep the unpleasant bavardage away from him for a while, until further attempts of ridicule emerged. Parliamentary opponents trying to embarrass the King came forward, their tales gaining momentum. Rumours surrounding the King reached officials. It was becoming impossible for the King's staff to dampen out the baneful humour. Critics of Henry were carrying out a serious character assassination, which the young King had not yet encountered in his short but successful rein. Still, he showed no signs of yielding his position on the throne.

Catherine was made aware by her entourage of duchesses of the unwarranted accounts that were circulating. Certain circles had made it clear for some time now that they believed Henry was holding too much power. They were now taking advantage of the tales of a young King and his treehouse to promote the proposal that decisions regarding the country should be made fairly, delegating decisions to landowners and gentry, who were growing frustrated by the King's lack of consideration.

It was Catherine who took it upon herself to discuss the critical whispers with her husband. She and Wolsey were of the opinion that the discourse should be allowed to take its course, and that it would soon be forgotten. More important issues would replace the languishing talks in parliament.

The Queen decided to wait till dawn to approach Henry on the balcony. It would be in her benefit to raise the matter with Henry in view of the oak. The King had been cleverly shielded by those loyal to him. He had no inclination of what Catherine was due to unveil. She approached it cautiously, knowing better than to sugar-coat the truth out of saving face.

Henry listened carefully to what was being put before him, waiting to hear the full content of the gossip of the courts before saying anything. Catherine brought with her two of her duchesses, believing, albeit naively, that their presence would force the King into a calmer, more rational reaction. No sooner had she finished relaying the tattle to Henry than he instructed the foresters to come immediately and fell the oak, demanding the tree in all its height is chopped to its base.

His wife pleaded for common sense to prevail, reminding the King of the dear squirrel family to which the Royal Oak is home. She would be distraught to see him inflict suffering on Roux and his family, those who had served him so faithfully over the years. But the King was overcome with anger. He began pacing up and down, pushing the women to one side as Catherine leapt to their defence. She tried to bring a calm to the proceedings, but the King wanted silence.

Catherine had noticed from the corner of her eye that Roux had attempted to cross over, but having seen Henry's outburst, had retreated back to his oak, perhaps postponing his visit until things had calmed down.

Henry was immediately wanting names of the offending parties but was told that there were too many to accurately place blame on one individual.

Catherine was regretting having involved the duchesses and made moves to clear them from the balcony. In the past, she had had plenty of success in making the King see sense. Now, however, it seemed there was little she could offer in the way of constructive words.

Henry could not control himself. The thought that he was the subject of mockery was too much to bear. Those who were perpetuating the blasphemous accounts would pay.

The gardeners were called in to move the squirrels, ordered to find another location which would suit their requirements. When successful, they were to report to her majesty, letting her know of the squirrels' new address. The location was to remain private, as the King was only now recovering from the ridicule.

Roux and family were moved over a period of three evenings. The gardeners had found a new location in a greenhouse in what Henry often referred to it as his secret garden. A name that the three men thought fitting of the rehousing.

Roux ceded to the move, aware that it was the best thing for his family's safety. He was unable to forgive the King for the vicious onslaught on the tree. It was clear to him that the monarch held little care for the welfare of him and his family, that their friendship meant nothing to Henry anymore. His pride being his primary and exclusive concern.

The move to the greenhouse signified a heart-breaking end to an important chapter in Roux's life. He watched as the men axed away at the tree, dismantling all of his hard work. The space opposite the balcony was now devoid of life, reducing the once grandiose landmark to no more than ruins, unable to sustain any wildlife.

Chapter Nine

Unification

After six months, Roux and Henry's relationship had not been repaired. They had been forced to accept the changes in their lives.

Roux was finding it difficult still to forgive the King and his unwarranted attack on his much-loved home. From what he could tell, the chopping of the Royal Oak had little to do with him, but nonetheless he was one to feel the wrath of the Henry.

Beatrix hadn't made so much of effort to make their current home as stately as the last. She believed now, having endured such misfortune, that it was more important to live in a comfortable, loving home than one which is admired by those whose opinions were of no concern to her. She didn't want to live in an exhibition. She wanted to live in a home, where it didn't really matter if you wipe your paws when you come in.

They had, during the move, lost their only son. Beatrix was pregnant again, and together they were longing for another boy. Someone who could assist Roux in his old age.

The foresters had made it their duty to replenish the little basket by the tree in the greenhouse with nuts, acorns and seeds, mindful that their new location wasn't in abundant of the foods the squirrel family needed. They had also taken it upon themselves to build a scarecrow outside, effectively keeping the birds away. They had also erected a fence around the old, nobbled tree, blocking off the means of entry for a number of predators. Gestures of genuine kindness.

On an extremely hot summer's evening, the family had sought shade in the nearby potting shed. Beatrix gave birth to a son, a new future to look forward to. The family had experienced their fair share of tragedy, having in their time lost two kittens. Beatrix was anxious. She wanted more than anything to keep her new-born alive.

Roux went straight to work on the essential maintenance of the greenhouse. He spent hours strengthening entrances and building the nursery. No expense spared, he wanted to ensure the best for his boy.

The gardeners had been anxious for some time, concerned that they hadn't seen the squirrels around much lately, until one bright afternoon when Beatrix decided that an hour in the daylight would do the young boy no harm. She chose a sheltered spot to sit with her son among the old trees.

The men were delighted, relived to see the family was okay. They melted in affection, these three hardened men of the land, enjoying the spectacle of the mother and son. While his wife spent some time in the sun, Roux took the opportunity of an uncrowded house to organise the interior of the home, for his own sanity. His once relaxing routine of roaming the garden and surrounding borders for food had now turned into a manic search, trying to cross everything off the comprehensive list that Beatrix sent him off with each day.

The family was complete. Roux threw himself into fatherhood for the third time, learning from his previous mistakes. His new son, Rioch, was fast becoming a strong young man. He stayed well within the perimeter of the garden, only venturing outside when his father led the expedition, even then staying close to him at all times. Life was shaping up for this family of squirrels.

Roux was determined to train Rioch in good time, conscious that his life was passing him quickly by. If predictions are accurate, he would live for an average of five years. Reaching the halfway mark, Roux had to prepare for the unthinkable. There was always a chance that life could be kind to him. With Beatrix's care, he could enjoy a longer life of six or seven years. Some squirrels had even lived for ten years, but those cases were rare, and tended to be the case only for those whose lives were undisturbed by human habitation.

Still, Roux was fit and enjoying his health.

Chapter Ten

A Royal Visit

The gardeners felt that the last thing the squirrels would accept easily was an eviction of their home in the greenhouse, which was in great need of repair.

As expected, the greenhouse came down easily. They had been careful to not go near the root of the old tree, so as to not disturb Roux and his family. But it dawned on them that the lack of shelter would likely have a negative impact on their life, the squirrels could no longer guarantee their security.

Roux and Beatrix were confused. They hadn't anticipated any work being done. They tried to keep the children in the back, away from the noise of the demolition.

As the men progressed with their work, starting to excavate the tree, they were surprised to find themselves in the company of the King's page. Following him was his majesty's equerry, carrying a heavy overcoat and a silver salver complete with nuts, seeds, and an apple core. The Queen's lady in waiting then turned the corner, following the small procession in line, clasping something too small for the men to see. The men stopped their work, anticipating the entry of the monarchs.

The King and Queen appeared together, and the gardeners removed their caps in due recognition of their sovereigns.

Henry and Catherine walked over to the men, accepting their acknowledgement and inviting them to continue with their important work.

The equerry handed the King the silver salver, usually taken on the balcony, and placed the coat around his shoulders. The Queen came forward as the lady in waiting placed the lock of the red hair on the salver, which together they had thought of as a gesture of goodwill. Catherine suggested that it might just inspire Roux to venture out.

Henry asked Thomas, the head gardener, if after digging out the trunk and roots he would place the remnants of the tree A few feet away from the burrow, so that he and his wife might sit.

Catherine took Henry's affectionately. The entourage was asked to leave them be, assured that they would call should they require any assistance.

The large tree stump was laid opposite the borough. The page set down blankets over the log and started to prepare some refreshments. The

King and Queen took their seats, draping blankets over their laps.

The first hour passed. Catherine, being keen on the palace gardens, had gone to stretch her legs, leaving Henry sat staring at the silver salver in the hope that it would   attract some attention at the entrance of the burrow. When the Queen finally reappeared, the page offered up some refreshments. The monarchs accepted, the King being in need of a pint of his favourite ale.

Henry was taking a sip from his pewter when Catherine gasped. Roux had appeared. She gently took the pewter from the King's hands, placing it on the ground beside him. They sat motionless.

Roux squeezed his shoulders through the narrow entrance. He spotted the two figures sitting on his old tree, blankets over their laps. He noticed that they were both sporting their squirrel brooches, affixed to their finery. The squirrel stood, his plume assuming its position, resting over his head. A sign of respect for his monarchs.

Still, he was uncomfortable. The excavation had frightened him, his whole family living in a nervous state. He was unsure of his next move. With no place to go, he was worried about his family. They had been happy in their surroundings, especially Beatrix. It would take some convincing for her to move somewhere new.

Henry could tell that Roux was nervous, having spent so much time with him on the balcony and in the treehouse. The fact that his old squirrel friend hadn't retreated gave him hope.

Although daunted, Roux began to remember his dearly spent time with the royal couple. There was a tenderness about them. He caught sight of the silver salver and the apple core. This warmed his heart, how he had missed his dear friend.

He thought it time to venture further forward. The squirrel made his way, slowly and cautiously, stopping several times before arriving at the salver. Henry didn't move a muscle for the entire time, looking away. He didn't want to make Roux any more nervous than he inevitably already was. He spotted Roux from the corner of his eye, darting back the way he came and diving down into the borough. When he looked back to the salver, the apple core had been whisked away.

Catherine wondered whether that was that. Would Roux make another appearance? Henry suggested he stay on his own, reluctant to leave the task to anyone else. She stayed for another hour, amazed that Henry had at last learnt to exercise patience. She was proud of him, pleased to see that she had had some impact.

Henry was left on his own then, sat on the tree, determined to see the wait through whatever the outcome.

As Henry sat enjoying his third pint, Roux appeared as if from nowhere, his wife at his side. Beatrix was immediately struck by the King's stare, which focused on her for some time. Henry finally moved, placing his pewter down at his side. Beatrix shot back down the burrow, but Roux didn't follow, so it was only a short while before she sheepishly re-joined the two old friends.

Roux took the first step then, heading back towards the silver salver to gather some nuts for Beatrix for her to give to the kittens, who she had left behind for safety. This went on for nearly fifteen minutes until the salver was emptied of all its contents. Roux went back down the burrow, returning this time with the remnants of the apple core and leaving it on the salver.

It was time for the squirrels to depart for the day. The King was confident in the progress they had made. Roux seemed more comfortable, feeling safer in Henry's presence.

The page packed everything away and Henry left the greenhouse, content that his day hadn't been wasted. His dear squirrel friends would always be welcome back on the balcony, for things hadn't been since the same since their departure.

Catherine felt that there was a void in Henry's life since he had made the decision to chop down the Royal Oak. Having repaired his friendship with Roux, the Queen wondered if he might consider allowing her to introduce the squirrel family onto the balcony on a more permanent basis. The long nest boxes had now been empty for over a year, and she felt it would make a perfect residence for them. The King took the proposal into consideration, eventually agreeing.

The Queen took over straight away, summoning the gardeners who had cared for the squirrel family. The three men agreed to make the move as smooth as possible for Roux and his family. The nest boxes were lengthened, ramps were installed, and the walkway was kept in place, but lowered to reach the remains of the oak, giving the family a route to the park.

News reached the Queen that Roux and Beatrix had now increased their family by one. Catherine took this as a good omen, now even more determined that the family should return to the palace and live under her umbrella of care.

The next stage of the plan involved the moving of the squirrels. It would be especially difficult to convince the family to move out of their settlement, and into one they saw to be riddled with misfortune.

It had taken Roux a long time to forgive Henry's actions, but he was thrilled to be welcomed back into the palace, even if the oak was now only a shadow of its former self. Its basic structure still stood, it was large and spacious. With the help of his son, they could renovate the trunk, reinstating themselves in their old home.

The trunk lacked shelter, which the squirrels would desperately need. Roux sought to address that first. He would race up and down the walkway each morning, in the hope that the King would notice him.

Eventually, Henry followed his friend down the walkway to the tree. It had rained some hours before, flooding the trunk. This wouldn't do for his old friend. He instructed the gardeners to build a cover.

The King's personal life took a turn for the worst as Catherine gave birth to their second child, only to lose it days later. Henry was in dismay, having proclaimed to the nation that he would at last have an heir. Fearing the humiliation, he placed the blame on Catherine, stating that it was she who was incapable of giving him a child to succeed him. The Queen, already broken from her loss, was bruised by her husband's bitterness.

Somehow, the King carried on with his duties, seemingly unaffected by the loss. His morning sessions continued. He would sit in his chair on the balcony, shivering from the cold as he enjoyed Roux's company.

Roux stood for loyalty. Henry was grateful for his daily presence, loyalty being something that so few outstretched to the King lately. Everybody around him was slowly being considered the enemy. Those close to Henry become anxious, nervously aware of his temper. People in ministerial and secretarial positions kept their distance, scheming and conspiring behind Henry's back, attempting to avoid his outbursts that were now a regular occurrence. The King had become prone to throwing the court and crown into daily conflict.

Still, in the eyes of the nation, Henry remained a good King. His military planning was sound, his justice was harsh but necessary. He was still popular among his subjects, who accepted the ways of his rule. But those in the know could not accept Henry's behaviour, they knew he was suffering privately.

This wise little squirrel realised only too well that he had lived the best years with the King, noticing the temperamental decline. Those times were now over. This was indication that it was time to move on, it was time to put his family first. After all they had been through, Roux understood that it was the work causing the King to act in such a way.

Roux knew that his time was passing quickly. His life had been a unique one, it wasn't typical for his species to live so harmoniously among humans. In his eyes, Henry was deceiving himself as well as others. The kindness had disappeared, as had his loving ways with his wife who, in Roux's eyes, had been wronged by the King. He knew that in his time, he had served his friend well. But those good years were dissolving now, and the future didn't look as bright as it once had.

Roux had spent valuable time and trouble teaching Rioch the ways of the world, leaving a legacy to be followed. He made sure Beatrix would be well looked after, and that his daughter should want for nothing. Most importantly, he made sure that they both knew to buck the trend, staying together even when their dear mother passes on.

Rioch had gone to enormous lengths to ensure that everything was in place for Roux to relax into retirement. Beatrix had made every effort to attend to his every need. Rianne took on her mother's mantle, so that Beatrix could join her son in gathering food for the coming winter.

Roux's sight was fading now. The trunk of the oak became his sanctuary. He rested there, reflecting on life. He knew he was loved by his family and that he had served them well.

Now, the time had come.

Chapter Eleven

Two Queens Grieve

King Henry now spent less time at Hampton Court, favouring a move to both Windsor Castle and Greenwich Palace as he was needed closer to London. The French war was escalating. He was making numerous trips to Portsmouth and Chatham each month to oversee the navy. It seemed his presence was required everywhere.

Hampton Court was, for once, languishing in peace. The whole palace had been shut down, leaving only a skeleton of staff for general maintenance.

Henry had, after everything, left Catherine at Hampton Court. She was expecting another child. Her apartments were the only ones open, her slimmed down staffing being the only ones to Work the palace. Catherine had to accept the loneliness that echoed through its halls. Out of sight, out of mind, is what Henry had intended by leaving her behind. But Catherine didn't give in. She had friends in high places, and still commanded authority. To her defence came religious leaders, retaliating to Henry's attempts at disbanding their union. Divorce would not be as easy as he thought.

Catherine spent many a day outside, making good use of the bench surrounding the Royal Oak that had remained in place despite the chopping. To fill her time, she read a lot and sketched, entertaining the few that were allowed to visit.

On one such day, as she was engrossed in her book, she heard some shuffling coming from the trunk. Looking up from her book, she saw Beatrix had settled nearby. A smile stretched across her face. How lovely it was to see her again, after all this time. She had often wondered whether she should make a visit to the balcony, but Henry had locked all access to his apartment.

The staff had relayed to her some time ago that the nesting boxes were still in place but seemingly unused.

Beatrix remained motionless. Catherine got the feeling that she wasn't merely passing the time of day but had come to tell the Queen something important. Catherine held her gaze, breathing gently. Both youngsters had now come out from the trunk and settled close to their mum. They seemed lost, despondent even, keeping their heads down. Looking at Rioch and Rianne reminded her of the torment she had felt in losing her two children, but the sight of Beatrix brought back happy memories.

She closed her book, signalling to her lady in waiting that it was time to go. As she turned her head, she noticed Beatrix and the kittens had disappeared. The lady in waiting collected the Queen's belongings from around the trunk. Just as Catherine went to stand, Beatrix reappeared. She made her way slowly and nervously down the bark, closely followed by Rioch and Rianne. The Queen, unsure of what was occurring, took her lady in waiting's hand for comfort.

Beatrix soon reached the bench. She hesitated, as if composing herself, and settled herself on Catherine's book cover, resting on her lap. Catherine sat very still, mesmerised at the squirrel's behaviour. With grace and calm Beatrix placed a small handful of rustic fur on the book cover and looked up at the queen, then quietly without looking back made her way back up the oak followed by her kittens, the Queen believed that she understood that this meant, as some had expected, that Roux who had not been seen for some time, that the inevitable had eventually happened.

She picked up the fur, stroking it softly. She thought of their first encounter, when Roux had so trustingly sat in the palm of her hand.

Thankful for the special gift, she gently placed it between the leaves of her book for safety taking some time to digest, savour, and recover from such an extraordinary moment

Back in the palace, the Queen selected a locket of her choice, opening the clasp and pressing the fur inside. She wore it daily, a tribute to her friend that had meant so much.

With Henry's consent, Catherine ordered that the Royal Oak be allowed to grow, restoring to its former glory so that the future monarch's would benefit from its strength and power enabling many of Roux's descendants to benefit in its grand interiors that made one very special family so happy keeping their majesty's in grace and favour.

Chapter Twelve

The First Queen of England

On February the 16th 1516 at The Place of Palencia in Greenwich, Catherine gave birth to her fifth child. To Henry's disappointment, she had borne another girl, but thankfully she seemed in good health.

Henry, at long last, was able to hold his head high, having finally an heir to his throne. He rejoiced with his wife for the blessing they had been granted, after having endured such grief.

The couple wasted no time baptising the child. She was named Mary at Greenwich, just three days after she was born. The anguish of not having a son quickly dissipated. Mary grew to be a beautiful child. She had a fair complexion, pale blue eyes and that famous red hair. A natural succession in the Tudor dynasty.

Henry adored his daughter. He was fast becoming a boastful father, leaving it to Catherine to discipline young Mary. She educated Mary, having her reading and writing in Latin at an early age. The young princess went on to study Spanish music and learning to dance under Catherine's expert guidance.

Mary lacked the guile of her Tudor ancestry, omitting that steel-like quality from her own behaviours. She possessed, instead, a loving nature, prompting her to return soft answers to her father's bouts of wrath.

The young Tudor treasured Hampton Court, loving the open spaces. An adventurous life outdoors suited her, giving her a new zest having found the confines of the London palaces dull and spiritless.

Henry once again opened up the balcony for a small reception party in celebration of his daughter. Unlike his past functions, only a handful of carefully selected guests were invited for the intimate gathering. Thomas Wolsey, her godfather, and the countesses of Salisbury and Devon, her godmothers were among the exclusive guestlist.

Halfway across the young, growing branches of the Royal Oak, Beatrix and her kittens were taken aback by the noise on the balcony. They hadn't heard of any palace festivities for a long while, not since before Roux's passing.

Beatrix decides to scale the ivy clad wall. She continues upside down for some yards before reaching the end, and bravely jumps onto the parapet, keeping her head and tail low, not wanting to be seen. She had a perfect view of the balcony. She signals over to her waiting kittens to take the same route. They do so nimbly, and more expertly than their mother had. They make the final leap of faith, joining their mother in the ivy, when they are alerted to a sudden cry.

It was the Countess of Devon, pointing excitedly to the squirrels for her children to see.

The scream shook Beatrix's confidence. She recoils into the ivy, waiting motionless until the balcony guests redirect their attention back to their celebrations. Henry keeps quiet. The last thing he wants is for people to know about his private visitations which he thought had concluded some time ago. Catherine speaks up, redirecting the conversation, taking the attention away from Beatrix so she and her young squirrels can go about their day.

The young squirrels lead their mother round the underneath of the parapet to the other side of the balcony. She followed them up over the wall, directly into the opposite stretch of ivy hanging further down, leaving no gaps through which they could be spotted.

Half an hour passes. The squirrels remain on guard for any unexpected movement. Beatrix was transfixed by the Queen. She is keen to descend onto the balcony and get closer to her majesty, remembering her kindness.

The kittens insisted she wait awhile. Henry had stepped away for a moment and they felt he could return unannounced. It would be safer if they all went down together.

The King returned, as the just as the kittens had anticipated. However, following closely behind him was Winona, now the assistant housekeeper to the Queen. She was carrying a silver salver, as she so often had.

Catherine looked at Henry, surprised to see him extending this kindness to their squirrel friends after so long. The surprise visit had reminded him of his neglected obligations, he explained, placing the salver at the end of the parapet for the family to enjoy.

The King hoped it would be the first of many more visits. For the squirrels, they were honoured to have been gifted their old favourites by old friends.

Henry hoped that his daughter would one day meet the three squirrels, and that she too could experience a friendship so dear and therapeutically so valued.

The Reason and In Memory Of...

I celebrated my half century by acquiring a farmhouse in the Peak National Park with twenty-one acres of land. A midlife crisis to abate the rigours of a somewhat strange but effective thirty-five years in the entertainment industry, brought on by an ever-increasing sense of aging.

Starting from scratch, with no previous experience appertaining to husbandry or the inner workings of a farm, and regretting not having had that necessary health check, I threw myself into the physical demands of a fourteen-hour day. It seems I was misguidedly attempting the impossible, but in some strange way enjoying it along with the swallows, the badgers and the foxes.

One afternoon in late winter, I received an unexpected visit from a retired solicitor from Stockport. He was now taking matters into his own hands and working from home. Having visited my ninety-five donkeys on several occasions, he had felt obliged to offer me advice relating to future plans. His first misguided suggestion was to enquire if I had made a will, as my age would require such security now. I stared at him as he came up with suggestion number two – had I thought of downsizing, as things could well take a naturally unexpected turn, which could swing the balance with the ability to catch me unaware. I felt an urgent impulse to stop him at this juncture, reminding him that he had not been invited to depress me in such a manner, and that I was sorry, but I could no longer assist him with his return journey down my mile-long drive because it was blocked with snow.

I had now to accept some home truths, although thankfully the word retirement had never been mentioned for fear of me becoming violent. But sadly, there was a modicum of sense in what I had been forced to listen to. After much discussion that I would rather not have had, we moved into a small but charming bungalow in the pretty village of Disley in East Cheshire.

There is no doubt that it was a shock to the system, but I was conforming to public opinion. Worse still, accepting defeat. Throwing in the towel, or in my case the flannel.

I devised an after-dinner talk which I thought would get me by, but after six months I had been adopted onto the circuit. We were travelling hundreds of miles a day to get to women's institutes that were not registered on any sat-nav, all mainly built on unregistered roads, bridle paths, talking from stately homes to an Anderson shelter.

On rare occasions that we were not travelling, I would sit in the conservatory enjoying the horticultural splendour of my wife's successful endeavours, having succeeded in turning our modest plot of land into a world heritage site.

Our garden had one immense treasure – a most magical oak tree, an unexpected gift to a small garden which spread a sensational canvas of leaves in the summer months, still giving the same immense pleasure in the autumn with abundance of acorns. The pleasure heightened as I was soon to be introduced to a pair of irresistible squirrels, who had become my non-paying tenants.

I have, at this stage, to admit being completely taken over by these two athletic rodents. The speed with which they manipulated their journeys, their balance on thin twigs which one could never imagine would support their weight, leaping from branch to branch, the amount of food they were able to collect in a suburban area. I was mesmerised by them as they sat upright in our flowerpots every day just outside the conservatory door, seemingly unafraid, demonstrating the correct way to shell acorns and other nuts they'd acquired. I watched in awe as the two disagreed about things. They never seemed to steal from one another, which made me believe one was male and the other female, but that wasn't apparent until later.

The oak was their castle, which made me spring into action to write a different book than those I had already published this year. I decided to commemorate the squirrel as best as I could. As my squirrels were aware of different colour, one being stone grey the other with black fur mixed with grey markings, I decided on a story of a red squirrel, as I understood that they could now be an endangered species and needed some support.

My research, mixed with my great love of history, led me to Hampton Court Palace. I was intrigued that red squirrels were mentioned in some books as having lived in the grounds during Tudor times. I was ready to uncover my story, bringing Roux to life and into your homes, as his friends had appeared so delightfully in mine.

The story of my squirrels ends on a sad note, as one day we noticed our male squirrel had been run over outside our house and left in the road. The mornings have never seemed the same since. As unbelievable as it may seem, his partner met the same fate some three weeks later. A tragedy. My oak has had no squatters since, but I keep my fingers crossed. It is such a desirable residence that it won't be too long before we receive new tenants.

So, here's Roux, just for you and all the other squirrels all around our country.